THE WORLD OF THE RACCOON

LIVING WORLD BOOKS
John K. Terres, Editor

The World of the

RACCOON

Text and Photographs by

Leonard Lee Rue III

J. B. LIPPINCOTT COMPANY

Philadelphia & New York

To the world's finest parents, mine.
Mae S. and Leonard Lee Rue, Sr.

CONTENTS

AUTHOR'S INTRODUCTION

I CANNOT REMEMBER a time since I was in my early teens when I did not have one or more raccoons as pets. I have watched, studied, photographed, hunted, and read about them. I have reviewed all that I know about raccoons and have tried to review everything that others know about them in an effort to make this book as readable, interesting, and informative as possible.

Raccoons have become so plentiful that almost everyone has seen one. If you haven't, you undoubtedly have seen a picture of one so that you would at least be able to recognize the animal should you come across it. I have no idea how many thousands of hours I have spent with raccoons, but to me it was time well spent. The raccoon is one of the most interesting and appealing animals that I know.

I wish that I could personally thank the countless number of people who over the years have been such a great help to me in acquiring and furthering my knowledge of the raccoon. Such a list would be too long, but my hope is that those people who have been so beneficial to me will see this book and realize that I am thanking them again.

There are a few people though that I must single out to thank. They are Felix Bajor, Jules Marron, and Fred Space. Special thanks

11

The World of the Raccoon

go also to my nephew Robert Rowe and to my son, Leonard Lee Rue IV. Lenny has ably assisted me in the taking of many of the photographs in this book.

Again, I am grateful to my editors Stewart Richardson and John K. Terres for their help.

And though I have said it before, I must once more thank my wife Beth for her unstinting time, effort, and help in turning my hand-scribbled pages into a readable manuscript and for putting up with me in the process.

LEONARD LEE RUE, III

Columbia, New Jersey
February, 1964

THE RACCOON

THE RACCOON is a mammal that lives in every one of the continental forty-nine states but only in the New World. It is a carnivore whose ancestry goes back 30 million years to the Miocene Age where it, and the bears, developed from the primal dog race that was then evolving. The Latin name for the raccoon, *Procyon*, meaning "before the dog," is thus a misnomer. The raccoon is closely related to the ring-tailed cat of the Southwestern United States and the tropical American coati.

The name "raccoon" comes from the Algonquin Indian word *arakun,* a shortened form of *arakunem* meaning "he scratches with his hands." The raccoon's habit of handling its food, particularly in water, has given rise to the belief that the raccoon always washes its food before it eats it. This is reflected in the second half of its Latin name, *lotor,* which means "washer." The German name, *Waschbär,* meaning "wash bear" not only describes the raccoon's food-handling habits, but also the fact that it resembles a little bear. *Waschbär* was a much more accurate name than one given by the early French, under the Sieur D'Iberville, who called it *chat sauvage* or wild cat. Today the French Canadians call it *le raton,* while the Creoles of Louisiana call it *shoui,* the name given to the raccoon by the Choctaw Indians of that region.

13

The raccoon searches for much of its food along the water's edge

The statement that a raccoon always washes its food before eating it generally starts arguments flying thick and fast. Today the consensus among most mammalogists and naturalists is that the raccoon is a "dunker," a "feeler," and an "investigator," but not a washer. My own personal observations bear this out.

I have fed captive raccoons many, many times. They invariably have taken meat I have given them, plopped it into their water pans, where they pulled, pummelled, and felt it until it was to their satisfaction. Then they ate it. Yet, frequently they grabbed the meat and retreated to a corner of the pen where they went through the same process without placing it in the water. In each case the meat was clean when they got it and did not need to be washed.

I well remember the time I gave one of my pet 'coons some soda crackers. The crackers were promptly dunked into the water, and dis-

integrated. With a look of consternation, the raccoon attempted to fish out the pieces to no avail. Those were the last crackers it ever put into water.

It has been claimed that the raccoon has no salivary glands and washes food to aid in swallowing. Leon F. Whitney, a Connecticut veterinarian, has found that the raccoon has well-developed salivary glands, thus disposing of this theory. Others have told me that their raccoons would refuse to eat food that they could not wash. I have never observed this among any of the raccoons that I have raised.

Much of the raccoon's food is secured either in the water or along the water's edge. If a raccoon handles muddy food in the water, it might appear that he is washing it, yet most of it, such as fish, frogs, crayfish, and mussels, would be clean when caught. I have also watched raccoons feed upon dead shad on a river bank only inches from the water and make no attempt to wash the fish. Moreover, at certain times of the year the bulk of the raccoon's diet may be caught quite a distance from the water, where it is eaten unwashed.

Of all the raccoon's five senses, the sense of touch is by far the most highly developed. The raccoon is a plantigrade animal that walks upon the whole foot, flat-footed, just as bears and man do. The soles of its feet are hairless and its toes are long, well separated, and tipped with long, sharp, recurved nonretractile claws.

The raccoon is insatiably curious. This prompts it to handle everything with its tactile, facile fingers. Its sense of touch is heightened when its fingers are wet, and this is probably the reason why the raccoon "fingers" its food in the water.

There are five toes on each foot which aid it in its tree climbing. Although the raccoon does not have an opposable thumb, the fingers are so dexterous that it can locate food by touch alone. While fishing for tadpoles, minnows, or crayfish in shallow water, a raccoon seldom if ever looks at what it is doing. While the fingers are nimbly feeling for and locating its prey, the animal, with a detached air, may be scan-

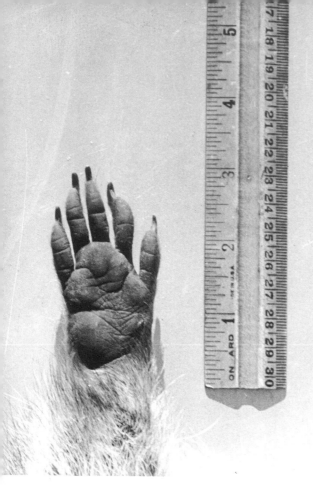

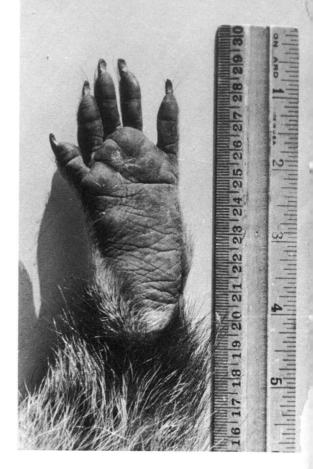

Right forepaw of raccoon   *Left hind paw of raccoon*

ning the riverbanks, studying the treetops, or simply staring ahead. Captive 'coons will often pick up tidbits of food that have dropped through the wire floors of their pen without being fooled by the pebbles upon which the food has landed even though they have to reach so far that they can't possibly see what they are doing. One raccoon that I had raised by bottle-feeding used to delight in going through my pockets while I held it. It would have made an excellent pickpocket because it had no trouble extracting a coin as thin as a dime. It didn't even have to bend its fingers to pick up the coins but would bring out several at a time, held separately between its fingers.

The forefoot on a large raccoon is about 2¾ inches long; the hind foot measures about 4¼ inches. The hind foot looks very much like a

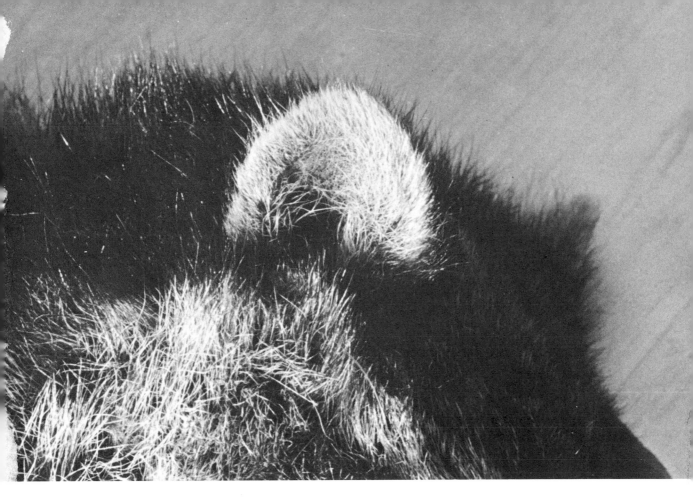

The raccoon's ear is short and rounded

human baby's foot except that the raccoon's toes are longer in proportion to the sole. Raccoon tracks in the mud look like the "little people" have been about in the night.

The sense of hearing in a raccoon is also highly developed. Although its pointed ears are not overly large, about 2½ inches long, the eardrums are well developed and its hearing is acute. Raccoons pay strict attention to any sound that is not in harmony with the natural noises of the forest.

Its eyes are of medium size, alert, black by day and orange-red or green by the shine of a light. Raccoons are classified as carnivores, along with wolves, dogs, foxes, bears, skunks, weasels, and the cat family. However, in their feeding habits they are omnivores: they eat not only meat but grain, insects, and berries. The raccoon's eyes are in the front of its head, giving it binocular vision. As the raccoon is mainly nocturnal, its eyes are equipped with a reflecting mirror built into the rear of the eye which enables it to see in the partial darkness of night. The available night light enters the eye and is absorbed; this stimulates vision. The light—infinitesimal though it is—that is not immediately absorbed is reflected by the mirror cells and passes through the retina again so that it has another chance of being absorbed. This gives the raccoon, and similar night creatures, a large gain in the utilization of the available light. Quite a few mammals have a reflective or special mirroring device behind the rod-and-cone layer of the eye. This device is called the *tapetum lucidum* and causes "eyeshine" in many animals that are active at night.

Raccoons can distinguish degrees of brightness but cannot distinguish colors as we know them. They see the world in monochromatic shades of gray.

The sense of smell is probably next in order of keenness. The raccoon does not hunt or stalk its prey as some predators do. Therefore, this sense does not need to be as highly developed as it is in some of the other carnivores. Some of its food, such as mice and ground-nesting birds, is located by scent. There are times when a raccoon will take up an object in its fingers and stuff it right against its nose so that the odors are literally drunk in.

The raccoon shows a decided preference for certain foods and will select these foods over all others when given the opportunity to do so. This indicates that the sense of taste also plays an important role.

Nature has provided the raccoon with 40 sharp teeth. It has 12 incisors, 4 needle-sharp canines, 16 premolars, and 8 molars. Food is not bolted down into the stomach as is the case with the dog and the fox. The raccoon thoroughly and completely masticates its food before swallowing it. While chewing, the raccoon usually curls its lips up

Internal "mirrors" reflect light causing eyeshine

20

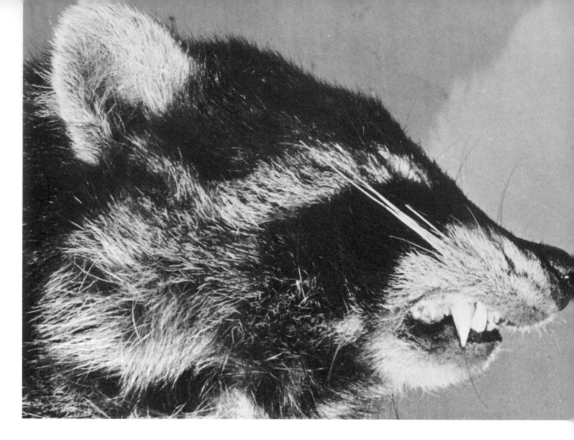

The raccoon's canine teeth are exceedingly sharp

Right side view of a raccoon's skull

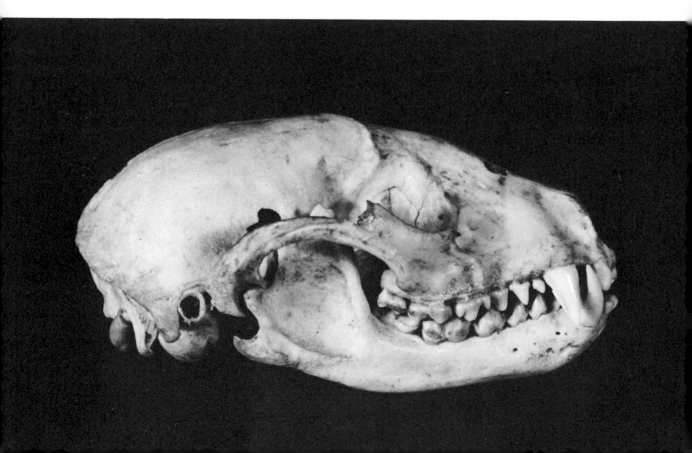

The Raccoon

and out of the way as if it dislikes the idea of messing up its whiskers.

Raccoons stand 9 to 12 inches high at the shoulders; body length is about 30 to 33 inches. Males are larger than females.

The raccoon is classified as a medium-sized mammal with the average weight of an adult about 12 to 16 pounds. Although there are claims of much greater weights, the majority of these unofficial estimates are made by hunters who have carried a dead raccoon for two to five miles through a swamp filled with briars on a pitch black night. By the time the hunter or hunters have gotten back to their car, they are willing to swear that each 15-pound raccoon weighs at least 35 pounds.

Top view of raccoon's skull

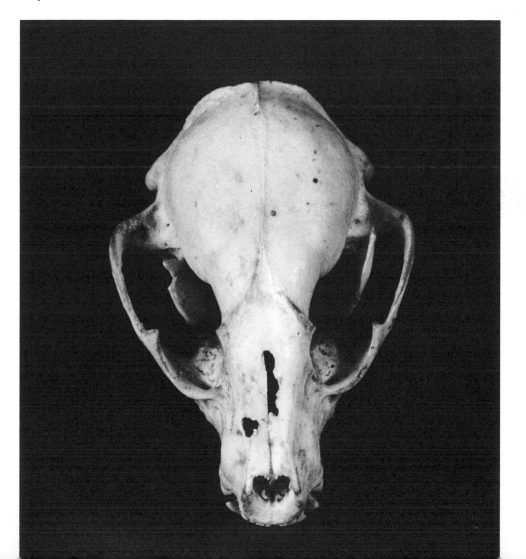

The raccoon curls back its lips as if to keep its whiskers clean

24

The Raccoon

After years of handling thousands of raccoons, both dead and alive, the heaviest one that I ever caught weighed 23½ pounds. In going through the records I have found a number of substantiated reports of actual scale weights. The greatest weight and size that I could locate was the record set by Albert K. Larson of Nelson, Wisconsin, on November 4, 1950. Mr. Larson shot a male raccoon that weighed 62 pounds, 6 ounces, and measured 55 inches long from nose tip to tail tip and 17¼ inches across the back.

Tolla Brown and Glen King of Sterling, Colorado, on November 11, 1960, took a raccoon near their town's reservoir that weighed 54 pounds on one scale and 56 pounds on another scale. Oliver J. Valley of Grant County, Wisconsin, took a raccoon that weighed in at 54 pounds even. W. W. Macie, the postmaster, storekeeper, trapper, and fur buyer of Sheldon Springs, Vermont, caught a raccoon that weighed 49 pounds on the store's scale. No dates were available on these last two records.

A Mr. Martin of Osseo, Minnesota, had a pet raccoon that was weighed officially in October, 1959, by the *Minneapolis Star and Tribune*. This animal weighed 57 pounds. Shortly afterward the raccoon escaped from captivity and as far as is known is still wandering around. It may perhaps be caught again, to establish a new record. In contrast, some of the adult raccoons of the Florida Keys weigh only 3 to 6 pounds.

Two features of the raccoon are known almost as well as the animal itself. They are the black "burglar's" mask that the 'coon has over its eyes and its bushy ringed tail. The tail is about 10 to 12 inches long and has from 5 to 7 black rings, with the terminal black tip being counted as one of the rings. The tail is not prehensile, as in the opossum and certain monkeys, and so cannot be used for grasping. However, it is often employed as a brace when the animal sits on its haunches and is used for balance when the raccoon is climbing or turning a sharp corner. It is also used for a reservoir to store surplus body fat.

The "burglar's" mask

In coloration the raccoon varies widely. Its geographic distribution has a lot to do with its color. The underfur comprises about 90 per cent of its hair, yet it is the longer guard hairs that give the animal its color. These guard hairs are oval in shape, if cut across the grain, and quite kinky or wavy in length. The general color of a raccoon is a grizzled brown, gray, black or yellow. The back usually has the darkest color, with the hair getting much lighter on the flanks, belly, legs and feet. The raccoon has a small, sharply pointed muzzle with a black nose. Its black mask extends in a 2-inch band across the eyes and down the cheeks stopping a little beneath the mouth line. The whiskers are white.

Raccoons of the southwest desert regions are a very pale yellow

The Raccoon

color. This is true of most mammals of that region. The lighter-colored fur reflects heat more efficiently. The largest and darkest 'coons live in the Pacific Northwest, the eastern ones are large and medium in color, while the palest 'coons are in the Colorado River delta and on the Florida Keys. Raccoons frequenting the salt-water marshes of our coastline usually have a reddish color. It was thought that this color was due to exposure to the sun, but it is now believed to be caused by the action of the salt that coats all of the vegetation through which the raccoon passes.

Both the albinistic and melanistic color phases occur in raccoons. The completely black, or melanistic, phase is said to be the rarer of the

The striped tail is probably the raccoon's best known characteristic

Albino raccoon

two. Black is usually dominant, and it would seem that there should be more of them than are reported. Mr. L. S. Russell of Cordington, Ohio, has successfully raised melanistic raccoons that have bred true and produced litters of melanistic young.

True albinos are all white with pink eyes. Yet the albinos I have seen had very faint yellow markings where the eye mask goes across the face and where the black rings would be on the tail. Acil B. Underwood has raised many albinos as well as true color pastel shades. The biggest drawback to all the work involved in a breeding program, such as is required to produce mutation in raccoon, is the lack of demand for such furs after they are produced. On the regular fur market the darker strains of the wild raccoons command a slightly higher price.

28

The Raccoon

Because of this the various states, when restocking raccoons, have tried to obtain the darkest-pelaged animals available.

Occasionally, a raccoon will be found that has no guard hairs at all on its body. This condition, also seen in foxes, is called a "Samson" pelt. That this characteristic can be passed on to the next generation has been noted in several young raccoons that were taken in this condition from a litter whose parents also displayed this unusual fur. This type of fur has little or no market value.

The raccoon is very vociferous and uses a large repertoire of sounds. When angry it hisses like a goose, snarls and growls. The snarling usually starts off low, is raised to a high pitch, and then is lowered again. When the raccoon is feeding in a family group, it may make a grunting sound or a quiet churring sound. The first call may mean that something edible is found. The churring sound is used to keep the family in contact with one another and is perhaps the most commonly heard call. Harsh variations of it are heard when young 'coons are hungry and a soft variation when they are full and contented. The sound is like a cat's purr amplified about ten times. Raccoons have a piteous cry when hurt, or when a little one thinks it is lost or is separated from its litter mates. When frightened and angry, they give a loud, piercing scream that will stimulate all other raccoons to action.

Another call, or perhaps I should say "song," is one that resembles the sound of a screech owl and is best described as a tremolo. It is often confused with the call of the owl, yet it has a deeper, more rasping tone. I truly believe that the raccoon utters more varied calls and does so more often than any other animal that I know. Many people, not realizing that the raccoon can make all of these sounds, often credit them to other animals. I have often been told about unidentified noises and screams that friends have heard at night. Most frequently the sounds are thought to be those of a wildcat. In my area of New Jersey, the wildcat or bobcat is very scarce, but you would never know it by

29

the number of people who think they have heard them scream. Perhaps these calls help to protect the raccoon. People may be willing to blunder out in the dark to shoot a noisy raccoon, but they certainly wouldn't want to tangle with a wildcat. Their fear leaves the raccoon free to go about its business unmolested.

Psychologists are constantly testing all sorts of creatures to find out how intelligent they are, how much they can reason, how much they can retain, and how much they can be taught. In the raccoon they have discovered a very apt pupil. Its native intelligence and natural curiosity coupled with its dexterity puts the raccoon high up on the mammal IQ scale.

After many tests, the psychologists have found that the raccoon is much smarter than a cat or a white rat but not quite up to a monkey, although it can perform many tasks designed to test the intelligence of the monkey. Most of these tests have to do with securing food, and the raccoon has learned to pull up food baskets on a string to get the reward of food that is placed in the basket. Raccoons chained by the neck will get food out of reach of their front feet by turning around and grasping it with the hind feet. The raccoon has no trouble pulling out corks, unfastening bottle tops, or opening door latches and turning knobs.

The home range of a raccoon is about a square mile if, in that area, its food requirements can be met. However, high local populations have been reported: 8 to 10 per acre in Mississippi; 42 per square mile in Illinois; and 100 taken from 102 acres in Missouri in 4½ days in winter. Possibly 1 per 10 acres is a good population in most areas. There is no record of migration other than the natural dispersal of the young in autumn or the extension of the raccoon's range by a few adventuresome individuals. When feeding along a water course, the raccoon may travel more than a mile because it never utilizes all the food available. To a raccoon "the grass is always greener on the other side of the fence," and it tends to move over there just as soon as it can.

30

The curious raccoon handles everything

Making tracks

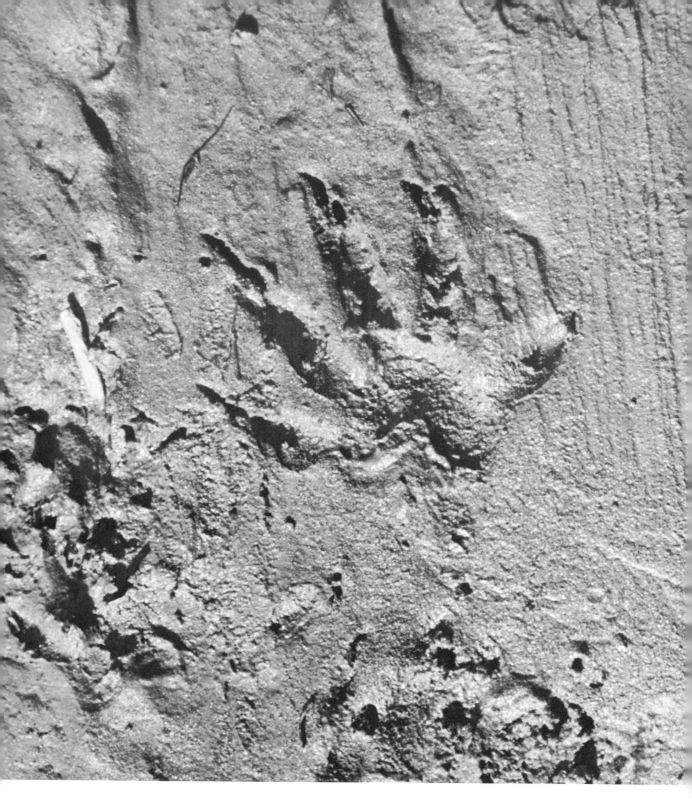

Track of raccoon's forefoot

Track of raccoon's hind foot

The World of the Raccoon

I have followed the tracks of an individual raccoon for much more than a mile while it was feeding along the shore of the Delaware River, which flows past my home. During the breeding season the males are on the go almost constantly and travel considerable distances each night. One raccoon I tracked on snow covered more than fifteen miles, but this must be considered exceptional.

In 1941, the Arkansas Game and Fish Commission undertook a raccoon restocking program. In the course of their work, 256 raccoons were live-trapped, ear-tagged, and then released on refuges in different parts of the state. The raccoons had all been taken from hilly areas, fed by small streams, and were released on flat river-bottom land. That the conditions were not to some of the raccoons' liking was shown by one raccoon that was retrapped seventy-five days later at a point 75 miles from where it had been released. Others that were also retrapped had moved various distances up to 33 miles. One female,

Regular gait of raccoon in a hurry

The Raccoon

however, was perfectly content with the change because she was discovered raising a family just 200 yards from her release point.

The greatest distance traveled by a raccoon was one that had been live-trapped, tagged, and released in the same spot in Marshall County, Minnesota, by the Game Commission in 1952. This animal was later trapped in 1955 by a farmer in Great Falls, Manitoba, Canada. The distance between these two locations is 165 miles. The farmer also noted that raccoons had been almost unknown in his area in 1950 but had been appearing in various local spots for the past couple of years. This would be a good example of a natural range extension of a species when food was available and there was no competition from others of its kind.

The traveling raccoon generally employs a slow, shuffling walk. This walk is interrupted frequently as it finds something of interest. At such times the raccoon picks up the object with its fingers while

Raccoon bounding at high speed

it sits upright on its haunches. The raccoon can also stand upright balanced on its two hind feet. When a faster gait is needed, the raccoon has a fast walk like a dog trot although it does not have the ability to travel long distances this way. When a real burst of speed is needed, the raccoon bounds along. Being a tree climber, it makes tracks that at this time look like an overgrown squirrel's. Both front and rear feet are used in unison, with the animal landing on the front feet and passing the body forward so that the tracks of the hind feet are placed ahead of those made by the forefeet. Top speed for the raccoon is about 15 miles per hour, but this cannot be kept up for any length of time. Almost any man can outrun a raccoon but this is not to say that the man can catch it.

Pound for pound, an old raccoon can beat any dog its size when it comes to a fight. They are very courageous fighters and have powerful muscles. Their compact size, short neck, and dense fur also gives them protection when fighting.

Raccoons feed in water whenever possible, yet they always seem reluctant to get wet if they can avoid it. They don't mind wading around but dislike getting their tails and backs wet. They are strong but slow swimmers. From walking along the shore opposite swimming raccoons, I would estimate their top swimming speed to be about three miles per hour. While swimming, they carry the head and tail as high as possible. A soaking-wet raccoon gives a much truer impression of its weight because its dense hair adheres to the body instead of being fluffed out. Upon emerging from the water, the raccoon will shake itself as hard as is possible, sending droplets of water cascading in all directions. This shaking is often so vigorous that the raccoon almost loses its footing. Even the tail is shaken violently.

The normal life span of a raccoon is from ten to twelve years. The oldest raccoon record is of one raised in captivity that lived to be fourteen years old. If there are records of greater longevity, I am not aware of them.

Raccoon emerging from water

SPRING

THE ICY WINDS blasted through the forest, rattling the few dead leaves that persistently clung to the gaunt oak tree. It was a day of retreat for all living things. Gone was yesterday's promise of spring. The temperature plummeted downward, and the ice relocked the water crystals that had almost escaped with the help of yesterday's sun. The day was dark and dreary. A small flock of goldfinches clung tightly to their precarious perches on the wildly swaying black birch limbs. Gusts of wind threatened to denude them of their fluffed-out feathers momentarily, and the warm air that had been trapped there was being forcibly replaced so often that the birds were becoming chilled. The life-giving sap, which yesterday had coursed upward in all of the trees, was hurriedly recalled and put back into storage in the roots. The mercurial days of March were with us.

High in a dry hollow, in a dying giant of a sugar maple, a female raccoon snuggled down for another sleep. The warm sun of yesterday had raised the temperature to the extent that she had shaken off her lethargy long enough to sally forth in the daytime. The softened snow left a trail for all to see, giving a complete description of her activities. It told of her fruitless search in the nearby cornfield where she had hoped to find at least a few kernels of corn that had been overlooked.

The World of the Raccoon

She had been doomed to failure even before she had started by her competitors—the deer, the squirrels and the mice that had had to brave the winter's cold in their continual search for food. The tracks showed where the raccoon had slaked her thirst at an ice-rimmed puddle before returning again to her den.

She really did not have to have food as yet because she still had some fat stores left beneath her skin. Early spring was the time of the year that most of the fat-storers would utilize their supply. Early spring was the time of increased activity and short food supplies—but today winter had returned so the raccoon curled tighter into a ball and slept.

April was kind to the land and to its inhabitants. The weather moderated steadily and the green growing things were thrusting themselves upward to claim their place in the sun. Many of the birds were returning from the South, and the swamps and marshes were filled with the calling of the red-winged blackbirds. At night the chorus of frogs voiced their pleasure at being freed from the cold of the pond bottom where they had spent the winter buried in the mud.

Every night of late, the female raccoon had been feeding. She stuffed herself with the shoots of the green grasses, instinctively knowing that they would act as a tonic for her.

In addition to the grass, the raccoon fed upon whatever frogs or insects she could catch. Earthworms now made up a large part of her diet and were easily gathered as they came up from their burrows, flushed to the surface by the showers of April.

Occasionally, while feeding along the swamp's edge, the female would encounter her mate. Usually they touched noses briefly and sniffed each other's fur. This formality over, they would go their separate ways, each intent upon finding something to eat. Their need for each other had been intense, then satisfied, back in February, during the breeding season in the North. In the South it may have been in December.

Marsh marigold

As the time of birthing her young drew near, the female became less active. Her size and weight were now a deterrent to the quick movements needed to escape an enemy. As her young were to be whelped in the den tree she was already occupying, she had only to await her appointed time.

Across the entire land, from ocean to ocean and from the north to the south, female raccoons were preparing to give birth. The timetable was not the same for all, for geographical differences had either speeded up or retarded the breeding season. But for all, some preparation was needed.

Where the old female's family had not broken up last fall, but had

41

spent the winter together for warmth and comfort, space was needed. If this were the case, the female, with her ears flattened, ruff raised, and canines exposed, turned on the yearlings and drove them from the den. Some of the pregnant yearling females must find new dens of their own. Now, all sorts of possibilities were explored. Hollow trees were ideal, but many of those forest giants had been felled by man's clean cutting and farming practices. Splits in limestone ledges, wood duck nest boxes, abandoned mines, unused drain tiles, and woodchuck burrows were pressed into service. Location of the nesting site was all

Typical raccoon den tree

Rock ledge being used by raccoons

that was needed because no effort to build a nest or to utilize any material other than that found on the spot was made. Only one exception to this general rule has ever been noted and that was in the case of a woodchuck's den, into which dry leaves were dragged by a raccoon who took it over.

In most dens, additional nesting material is superfluous. Most of the tree hollows have a considerable amount of soft, rotted wood particles in them, and the earthen dens have a soft layer of dust.

The average raccoon litter is four or five, but the number may be from two to seven. Birth occurs sixty-three days after breeding has taken place. The little raccoons weigh about two ounces at birth and, although blind, are fully furred. The fur is short and thin, and the black mask and the rings on the tail may be missing. The mother is very solicitous of their welfare and licks them thoroughly with her tongue until their fur is dry.

The female has six nipples on her underside, and the little ones begin to nurse as soon as possible. I can find no record of the butterfat content of raccoon's milk, but it is safe to assume that it is much richer than cow's milk because of the smaller quantity produced. It is sufficient, however, for the needs of the young raccoons because they thrive and grow rapidly on it. The mother in nursing may lay on her side or on her back like a cat with kittens. As her babies become stronger, the mother may sit upright, with her back braced against a wall of the den, and nurse her young as bears and woodchucks often do.

The mother takes complete care of her young, with no assistance from the father. In fact, the father is not even allowed near the den. If the male should become inquisitive and attempt to enter the den, he is sure to be driven away by the enraged mother. The fury of a woman scorned cannot even be compared with the fury displayed by a mother in defense of her young. And well may the female raccoon be alarmed at the appearance of her mate. Although it is not an habitual occurrence, there are many records of the male raccoon's killing the young ones and even eating them.

Cannibalism is the exception, and it is believed that the male raccoon does not recognize the young as his own. Apparently they represent interlopers to him, if not downright competition.

Wind shrieking through the trees, storm-tossed branches rubbing together, and the pealing of thunder, accompanied by bolts of lightning, do not alarm the mother raccoon. These are sounds to which she has become accustomed. Yet let there be the slightest scraping or scratching on the bark of the den tree and the mother is quick to investigate. The size of her antagonist means nothing to the mother raccoon. On two different occasions I have been chased off of a den tree by an angry female raccoon who did not want me around there.

44

Baby raccoons snug in their den tree

Although I meant no harm, I had no way of transmitting this to the raccoon. I will not say that the raccoons charged at me, but I *was* trespassing. When they growled and came out of their den holes, I left.

If disturbed too much or too often, the mother will move her youngsters to another location. She picks up each baby in her mouth, one at a time, by the scruff of the neck and carries it off. When the babies are small, she has no trouble carrying them from the den tree to the ground. When they are too large to carry, she picks up what

45

she can of each one and drags the rest of it along. If she becomes thoroughly frightened for the safety of her young, she may kill them herself and eat them. This is particularly true of females kept in captivity who become highly nervous in their unnatural surroundings at such times.

At this time, raccoons are most vulnerable to fire. It is fortunate that in spring there is usually enough rain to keep the woodlands damp. Saturation of the woodlands from the melting snows and spring showers combine to reduce forest fire hazards to a minimum. Occasionally the winter's snowfall is slight, the rains of spring do not come, and a dry wind sucks up what little moisture there is. The stage is then set whereby one careless act by man with fire, or a bolt of lightning from the skies, can turn the countryside into a blazing inferno.

A ground fire may race through the area without too much apparent damage to most of the trees although it burns fiercest in hollow trees. The hollow part acts like a chimney as the fire burns and the heat rises, causing a draft that fans the flames to greater intensity. Since hollow trees are the preferred den sites of raccoons, the helpless babies are often trapped. Some adults may save themselves; others refuse to abandon their offspring and perish with them.

One female raccoon in Texas never had to worry about forest fires. Hollow trees were a rarity in the area, and the conservation officials had put up a number of nail-keg nesting boxes to attract wood ducks. The entrance holes were large enough to allow raccoons to enter the boxes. Several moved right in and made themselves at home. One box, however, had been nailed and wired to a tree that stood completely surrounded by water, with the nearest land 20 feet away. This did not deter one determined mother raccoon. She plunged into the water and swam out to establish it as her chosen home. There was a great deal of algae growing in the water and her constant passage through it made two clear-cut trails from land to the tree.

Spring

By the time baby raccoons are ten days old, the facial mask and other color patterns are very plain, and they closely resemble their mother. Although they are unable to see, the babies crawl about and spend a good bit of their time squalling for food. They move with a spiderlike motion with the legs held greatly extended. This is a reflex climbing action and the little ones could hold on to the rough bark of a tree if placed there. At this age they do not have the strength needed for actual climbing.

The eyes of baby raccoons open about eighteen to twenty-three days after the animals are born. Their vision not being developed yet, they have trouble focusing on objects. Accurate sight is not important at this stage because they are still in a dark den, protected

Note the "spiderlike" climbing technique of the young raccoon

and fed by their mother, and surrounded by the warmth and reassuring sounds of their litter mates.

Little raccoons spend a great deal of their time sleeping, usually in a big pile, sharing each other's body heat. When one of the top layer of babies becomes cold, it just shifts around until it has gotten to the bottom of the heap. The weight of its brothers and sisters is not heavy enough to cause it any inconvenience.

The mother spends most of the daytime hours with her young, going forth after dark to seek the food that she needs for her own use and to continue her supply of milk for the babies. At first she leaves the babies for as short a time as possible, foraging for food

Raccoon feeding on little sunfish

close to the den tree. As time goes on, however, she is forced to hunt for food farther afield.

In the late spring the bulk of the raccoon's diet is composed of animal matter. This is not entirely by preference. Corn, berries, and other plant foods are not readily available. Now crayfish are the number one staple. To secure these succulent crustaceans, raccoons wade in every watercourse, be it slow-moving or swift. Crayfish lurking under rocks or in crevices are discovered and plucked from their lairs by the raccoon's nimble fingers. The only thing that saves the crayfish tribe from extermination is the fact that many of them frequent deeper water and escape the raccoon's search. It is amazing to see the rapidity with which a crayfish is consumed. Grasping it around the head, the raccoon sits up and stuffs the tail into its mouth. Its sharp teeth make short work of the crayfish's exoskeleton and outer shell; meat and all are eaten. The thorax is eaten next, and the rest may be discarded. If food is scarce, the head will also be eaten, with only the claws thrown away. The raccoon pays little attention to the crayfish's claws even when the creature is alive and using them for defense.

In shallow pools, raccoons capture shiners and various kinds of minnows. Attracted by the silver flashes on the fishes' sides, a raccoon will wade into the pool and sit down. As its nimble fingers search along the bottom, the sediment is stirred up until the water becomes murky. The fish take advantage of the darkened water in an effort to hide. Some will actually attempt to hide in the raccoon's long hair. The slightest touch on its hair spurs the raccoon into action, and soon a fish dinner is being eaten.

Raccoons have also been observed hooking larger fish from shallow pools with their claws. When a fish is seized, the raccoon usually bites its head. Instinctively it knows that this is the quickest way to immobilize its slippery prey.

While most raccoons will wait until darkness before they come out of their dens, those along the salt-water tidal marshes are geared to another clock, especially those in Florida. Their activities are governed by the tides. Well they know that the receding tide will leave a wealth of food stranded on the mud flats and in the shallow pools. So regardless of the hour, they are out reaping the sea's harvest. Because the ocean is usually very generous with its bounty, these raccoons have a rather easy life. At times the deadly "red tide"—an organism that kills fish—occurs, and millions of fish die and are washed up on the Florida beaches. When this occurs, all of the raccoons in the country couldn't possibly consume all of the available food. But the raccoons in the area gorge themselves trying.

In coastal areas where there are no trees at all, raccoons usually make their dens in tussocks of high grasses or may even take over an abandoned muskrat house. In the spring raccoons may be especially destructive to young muskrats. The adults have no problem with the raccoon because they are able to swim away. However, the baby muskrats lie helpless in their grass houses. It takes only a few moments for the marauding raccoon to tear through the roof and devour them.

This predation is so serious in some sectors that the very existence of the muskrat is threatened. In the tidal marshes of North Carolina's Currituck Sound the raccoons have broken into more than 90 per cent of the muskrat houses and have reduced the total muskrat population as much as 95 per cent in a five-year period. The damage is greatest in May and June, at the height of the muskrats' reproduction cycle. Few houses are broken into in November or December because raccoons know they cannot catch the agile adults. Muskrat dens in river or stream banks are seldom destroyed because the raccoon is not a deep-digging animal. Rice rats and other small rodents that may be nesting in the walls of a muskrat house are also killed and eaten by raccoons.

Raccoons living in such areas often live and nest in the muskrat houses. Living in the marshes, they change their lives accordingly.

Baby muskrats are vulnerable to predation by raccoons

Muskrat house

Nesting mallard hen

Nesting whistling swan

Baby cottontails are frequently eaten by raccoons

In the Horicon Marsh near Horicon, Wisconsin, raccoons have been found nesting in muskrat houses at distances of 450, 1000, and 1300 feet from the nearest dry land.

Muskrats are not alone in bearing the brunt of the raccoons' predation in marshes. Again at Horicon, it has been discovered that raccoons are responsible for 34 per cent of all the duck nests that are destroyed. The toll can be attributed to raccoons, for their pattern of egg-breaking usually identifies them. In opening an egg, a raccoon bites it in half so that half of the eggshell is left. The shells are usually scattered over an area of about 6 square feet. If a large rock or log is handy, the raccoon often carries the eggs to the top to eat them. It is not that the raccoon likes a view while eating its dinner but rather

53

The baby pheasant and other ground-nesting birds are preyed upon by raccoons

that it is using the height as a lookout point, to observe its surroundings for potential enemies. The raccoon frequently tears the duck's nest apart because it has an instinct for fingering and handling everything possible. In the process, the 'coon may lose a hair or two, and the long, black-tipped hairs identify the predator for the naturalist.

The nests of red-winged blackbirds, marsh wrens, and any other birds that the raccoons can locate will be raided and the eggs or young eaten.

The marsh dwellers, while bearing the brunt of raccoon predation, do not have its undivided attention. Its flat-footed shuffle in search of food takes the bandit through the forest and field. Baby rabbits, covered by their mother with a blanket of her fur and dead grasses, are also eaten. Baby squirrels, high in their leaf nests in the treetops or in cavities are preyed upon. Ground-nesting birds are especially vulnerable prey. Grouse nest in the same habitat that the raccoon favors for its home. Bob-white quail and ring-necked pheasant

54

seem to prefer to nest along fence rows or at the edges of small "islands" of brush growing around rocks or other obstacles. Raccoons
follow fence rows when traveling through cultivated fields because
the brush provides cover and a hiding place if necessary. This practice, of course, increases the chance of those birds' nests being discovered. Birds nesting in trees also fall prey to the raccoon. However,
the predation of raccoons is spread over the population of many kinds
of birds and mammals. If at times the 'coon may seem highly destructive, we should bear in mind that it is only one of many predators
that serve to hold down the population. One of the rules of life is
that something must die in order to provide food for something else
to live. It is a seemingly endless chain, with each of the larger creatures preying upon the smaller ones. Complex as it is, predation is a
part of the orderliness of nature, in which the raccoon is simply playing its allotted role.

*Eggs of tree-nesting birds, such as these of the crow, are also
eaten by raccoons*

SUMMER

THE LUSHNESS OF SUMMER is ample proof of a benevolent creator. The earth gives forth of its bounty in a season of plenty that is far beyond the needs of its inhabitants. Stems, stalks, twigs, branches, and boughs are laden with the seeds of promise. These seeds will not only replenish the world of plants but enable the world of animals to survive, by providing food and cover for them.

The hot days and the cooler nights cause the river beds, ponds, and lakes to be shrouded each morning in a gossamer of mist. Spider webs, bejeweled by the dew, rival the beauty of precious stones. Early in the morning, before the sun bounds into the sky, the passage of each creature may be plainly followed by trails blazed through the wet grasses.

The fragrance emanating from the various blooms is heady stuff. The breezes from the farmlands are freighted with the odor of new-mown hay, while the lighter, sweet scent of the honeysuckle seems to permeate one's very being.

Now the female raccoon takes extra precaution before she leaves the snug shelter of her hollow den tree. When she goes hunting each night, she is followed by her young family. As the evening shadows lengthen, she pokes her head out of the den and attempts to identify

A mother raccoon peering from her den

A dew-bejewelled spider web

Backing down   *A head first descent*

and catalogue the various scents and sounds. Her black nose wrinkles as it strains the breeze for a telltale scent of danger. She cocks her sharp-pointed ears forward and back, forward and back, as she tries to detect an unfamiliar sound that will warn her of danger.

The distant barking of a dog means nothing to her because the barking is in its customary place and direction. The whirring wings of the darting nighthawk, feeding upon insects, is reassuring because the presence of the bird precludes any danger of a great horned owl slipping into the area undetected. At last, convinced that nothing seems amiss, the female descends to the ground followed by her little ones.

When climbing, the raccoon may back down the tree in an upright position, or it may come down head first. Most of the tree-climbing animals have the ability to turn the hind feet out and completely

58

backward. The claws then dig into the bark, and the back feet are moved downward one at a time. The feet are also used alternately when the raccoon backs down a tree.

In climbing a tree, a raccoon will alternate the feet unless it is in a hurry; then it literally gallops up. The forefeet grab as high as possible, while the back feet shove the body upward. The raccoon does not have the agility of a squirrel but can climb with great speed. Even animals as large as the black bear can climb with this galloping motion when hard pressed.

Many times when a raccoon is climbing out on the branches of a tree, it will lose its footing and start to fall. With a lightninglike movement it will catch the branch with its feet and claws and hang on even though it now hangs upside down. If the limb has a branch or fork in it, the raccoon will usually be able to pull itself upright and resume its journey. If no fork is handy, it merely climbs along the limb, upside down like a sloth, until it reaches the trunk of the tree and then resumes its climb.

Raccoons will run along the tops of large limbs as if they were sidewalks. It is almost impossible to shake a raccoon out of a tree. It usually has to be pushed out with a stick or pole. Often the raccoon will climb out to the very end of a branch where its weight will cause the limb to bend far down. I have seen a raccoon descend a tree by bending each branch downward until it reached the branch below. I have also seen a raccoon hang from a branch by its hind feet as it looked around below to plan its next course of action. Both red and gray squirrels often feed in this position.

Loose bark sometimes causes a raccoon to fall. It is seldom hurt, or at least it does not appear to be, as it gathers itself up and scrambles off. Mother raccoons seem to recognize this danger to their young and have been seen removing loose bark from the den tree, possibly to guard against such a fall.

Joseph Vida of Harmony, New Jersey, told me that he was sit-

Raccoon climbing along small branch, falls, catches itself and then continues upside down

Raccoon walking along large limb

ting in his back yard under a big maple tree enjoying a cool evening breeze when the peace and quiet was suddenly shattered by pieces of bark that came rattling down. When Joe got up from his chair to see what was causing the disturbance, the noise ceased. The next evening the same thing happened. Joe could not see to the top of the tree. Going into the house and looking out a second-story window, he discovered that a large female raccoon had a family of young ones in a large rotted hole in the maple. On different occasions he witnessed the mother raccoon climb out on the trunk of the tree and either chew or pull off the loose pieces of bark. I, too, have seen the red scars on maple trees where bark has been removed, yet I always believed that the pieces had simply worn off.

Baby raccoons usually stay in the den until they are about eight to ten weeks old, although captives have come out of the den when

Raccoons often descend a tree by bending down the outermost branches

63

The World of the Raccoon

seven weeks old with weights of only 2 pounds. At this time they try to test their climbing ability and begin to venture forth from the den. Like the human mother whose child has just started to crawl, the raccoon mother is now very busy rescuing her offspring from the predicaments that they get themselves into. Mother raccoons have been known to adopt other baby raccoons that were orphaned by their mother's death and to raise such young with their own.

A baby raccoon was once observed climbing out on a limb that was over a slow-moving stream. Losing its footing, it fell into the

Baby raccoons

water with a loud plop. As it popped to the surface, it screamed with fright and the mother raccoon dashed out of the den and down the tree. By this time the bedraggled baby had reached the shore and was clambering out. The mother nuzzled her youngster to check it for injuries. Finding none, she returned to the tree and began to climb, followed by the baby. The little one did well until it got about two-thirds of the way up, when it became either tired or scared. It began to squall, and the mother, who had reached the den, had to come back down for it. She got below the baby and with her paws

Baby raccoons venturing forth from the den

on either side of it and her chest below the baby's body, she started to climb upward with the little one, which was using its own power but drawing its confidence from its mother.

Like kittens, baby raccoons will often climb to the very tiptop branches and then sit there and cry for help. Most baby animals find it much easier to climb up than to climb down. Once the baby raccoons start to climb readily, however, they travel in either the upright position or the upside-down one with equal facility.

Although a raccoon spends a great deal of time up in a tree, it does very little hunting there. The tree is for sleeping, resting, escaping from danger, and it is used as a den. A raccoon loves to sunbathe, often in a tree. I have seen raccoons on summer days stretched out on a good-sized limb with their feet dangling over the side. They often utilize crows' and hawks' nests for their siestas, or sometimes they clamber up on top of a squirrel's leaf nest. Adult males will often use these nests instead of a den hole. When a raccoon has enough space, it will lie on its back. At times it will shield its eyes with its paws to keep out the bright light, while at other times its legs are just flopped around anywhere as if they were disjointed.

Sometimes the raccoon will settle down in the crotch of a tree or where a large limb joins the trunk at an acute angle. I have also seen them asleep in tangles of wild grape vines growing in the top branches of a small tree.

Baby raccoons spend a good part of their time playing. Games of tag in the treetops are great favorites, but it is when the babies are on the ground that the action really gets rough. With a great amount of growling and squealing, the youngsters charge at each other in mock battle. Occasionally a hit will bring forth a yelp of pain.

The little ones wrestle and practice the fighting holds and positions they will utilize in earnest as adults. Frequently they hunch up their hindquarters, lower the fore parts of their bodies, spread their forelegs wide apart, and flatten their ears to their heads. In this posi-

Learning to climb

A good spot to stop and rest

Mother raccoon teaching her young to forage

tion they can take a tremendous amount of pressure before losing their balance. At other times they will rear up on their hind legs and with forepaws spread apart, await the charge of one of their litter mates. Closing in, they grasp one another and roll and tumble about on the ground. Frequently two or three of the youngsters will gang up on a single one. If the mother thinks that the playing is getting too rough or if a baby is injured, she will put an end to their activities by heading straight into the middle of the melee and cuffing them into submission.

The mother really must work hard now, because she has to teach her young ones the things they need to know in order to survive, and protect them while they are learning. Animals do many things instinctively, yet, like people, some are smarter and more successful in their endeavors than others. What they learn, mostly by example, speeds up the process of their being able to fend for themselves.

Young raccoons nurse for about fourteen weeks after birth and are then weaned. This is a gradual change, started as soon as the little ones are able to leave the den and follow after the mother. Very little

68

A tasty tidbit

Bottle baby

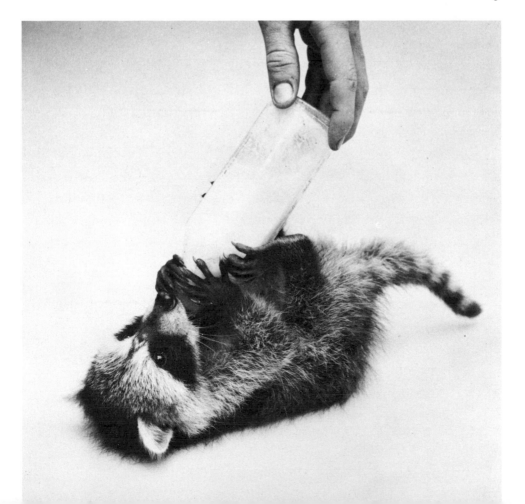

The World of the Raccoon

food is ever brought back to the den for the young ones, so that milk is their mainstay up to the time they are weaned. The babies shed their milk teeth and also get their permanent teeth about that time.

Young raccoons that I have raised on a bottle were always very greedy and would snatch at the bottle and slurp down four to six ounces in a short time. They usually worked the milk up into a froth that bubbled out of the sides of their mouth and all over their nose up to their eyes. They preferred to take the bottle and hold it in their paws on their chest while they lay on their backs. Occasionally they would hold the bottle with all four feet. If you picked the bottle up at such times, they just tightened their grip and rode along with the bottle without slowing down their feeding.

Pickerel frog

Summer

In summer the raccoon's diet consists mainly of plant products. Reports from Iowa and Illinois, where seasonal checks have been made of both scats (dried feces) and stomach contents of raccoons, have shown that vegetation forms about 72 per cent of the animal's diet. Some records showed it to be as high as 80 per cent.

Berries are eagerly sought and eaten: wild strawberries, raspberries, blackberries, blueberries, gooseberries, mulberries, pokeberries, and hackberries are among the most common. In lesser amounts, raccoons eat bunchberry and wintergreen berries. They also eat cherries, both wild and cultivated, and peaches and plums. Farm produce and garden patches will be raided for peas and potatoes. The most irresistible item in the raccoon's diet is sweet corn in the milk. When the

Slimy salamander

golden kernels are swollen to the bursting point, raccoons go on a corn-eating binge. They destroy far more than they eat in their anxiety to get at the next ear.

To get the corn, the 'coon climbs up the stalk, which usually breaks down under its weight. The husk is shredded and the kernels are promptly chewed off. At such times the cob is soft and tender and the raccoon may eat the end of the cob too. In hot weather raccoons do not eat much because they do not need calories to build up body heat.

Crayfish remain a staple in the summer. In the wet meadow grasses raccoons have little trouble catching frogs, which often forsake ponds and streams at this time to live in the meadows. They are much more vulnerable here than they were when they had deep water to escape into. Tadpoles swarming in the pond shallows in summer are so numerous that even the most inept baby raccoon seldom has little trouble catching them. When hunting for crayfish in streams, raccoons often locate hellgrammites, which they also promptly eat. Hellgrammites are the larvae, or immature forms, of the Dobson fly.

Along coastal areas, raccoons fish for eels and also consume many clams and oysters. Shellfish are sometimes hooked out of the water before they can close their shell. At other times raccoons chew at the hinge of the shell and force it open.

Fish stranded after high water has receded are a real bonanza, as are those trapped in small pools by a drought. Shad on the east coast and salmon on the west coast head up fresh-water streams to spawn and lay their eggs. Afterwards, the spent adults usually die and drift downstream to litter the shoreline, providing a cafeteria not only for raccoons but for all types of fish-eating wildlife.

Opposite my home there is a large island called Poxono, in the Delaware River. Having many large trees suitable for denning, Poxono supports a large number of raccoons. On one of the sandy beaches I set up a movable photography blind and baited the area with dead shad. I wanted to get photographs of turkey vultures feeding on the fish, but because of the large number of dead shad all along the river I was doomed to failure. The vultures were already gorged and not feeding.

Luck did not completely abandon me because I was able to get some good raccoon photographs instead. With the island virtually unmolested, raccoons often came out late in the afternoon to feed along the shore. As my blind had been sitting there for some time, they had become accustomed to it. While I was in the blind, I never noticed the raccoons being alarmed by my scent.

On one occasion a large male came out and fed upon the dead shad that I had placed there as bait. He sniffed the fish all over, but there was no human scent on the fish because I had speared it and carried it there on my knife. Although the fish was only a foot or so from the water's edge, the raccoon made no attempt to wash it. He did feel or pat it all over with his paws however. He then clawed out the eyes and ate them and then chewed off the nose. I have noticed many times that this is the usual pattern—no matter what creature the raccoon eats; the eyes are eaten first. After these parts were devoured, the anal gland was pulled and chewed apart and the entrails dragged out. Then the belly was chewed into and the remainder of the fish eaten. Since shad have very large, heavy scales, he may have found it easier to enter the fish through the natural body openings than to chew through the middle. While feeding, he was very alert, constantly looking around while chewing the pieces he had bitten off. Occasionally he would stop all movement and stare intently in the direction of a sound that I could not hear. He frequently looked back over his shoulder to make sure that nothing was sneaking up on him from behind. Perhaps his vigilance was intensified because it was daytime. After a time the sound of an approaching motorboat on the river caused the raccoon to leave. He just picked up his prize and carried it off to a protective jungle of ferns on higher ground.

73

Summer

On several occasions an old female and her babies came out to the shoreline to feed. By the time the little ones were large enough to follow after the mother, the shad run was over. The few fish that occasionally washed up did not seem to interest the family. Nor did the canned dog food that I had buried and lightly covered with sand. Instead, the raccoons seemed to be much more interested in something they were digging up from the river mud, although I never did identify what it was they were eating. They chewed on some water plants, but it seemed to me that they were picking up pebbles. The youngsters were not yet weaned and they seemed more interested in playing than they were in searching for food. Their attitude would have been different if their milk supply had been shut off. The mother

Feeding on shad stranded by high water

Family feeding

was constantly feeding or searching for something to feed upon, giving further proof that what she ate had to provide for the three of them.

On another occasion I saw a raccoon discover a box turtle that had just lumbered out on the beach from the high weeds on the river bank. Sensing a free meal, the 'coon hurried over to investigate. Grabbing the turtle, it bit at the head, which was promptly withdrawn. Not to be thwarted the raccoon felt for one of the turtle's legs and tried to grab it, but the turtle pulled it in. The raccoon tried for the legs on the other side and these, too, were withdrawn. At this point the turtle became tired of being poked at, so it slammed its shell shut.

The raccoon, not about to give up so easily, turned the turtle over and over like a plaything. At last convinced that it had been out-maneuvered, the raccoon dropped the turtle and went on about its business.

Most turtles would not have been that lucky. However, a large snapping turtle would be more than a match for a raccoon. Nevertheless, many species of turtles are regularly eaten by raccoons. In South Carolina, observers discovered that raccoons were catching and eating mud turtles and yellow-bellied turtles that had come up on land to lay their eggs. Researchers found that more than 50 per cent of the nests of these turtles were discovered and dug out by the raccoons. Many adults had been killed as well. Raccoons killed the turtles by biting their heads off. They were then eviscerated; only the hollowed-out shell was left. In Louisiana and Mississippi, turtles lay their eggs on levees, which frequently form the only high, dry ground. Of this situation the raccoons are quick to take advantage.

In my own area, wood, mud, yellow-spotted pond, musk, and eastern painted turtles are commonly killed by raccoons. The musk turtle is the least preferred, possibly because of its odor. While many turtles can escape raccoons if the water is deep enough, a prolonged drought will lower the water level and they are easily caught in the shallow pools.

Raccoons raid garbage cans all year round, but summer sees the peak of this activity. Many city dwellers have summer cottages or homes in the country or around woodland lakes. Unwittingly they add food scraps to the raccoon's bill of fare. Many people have been rudely awakened, some even terrorized, by the loud banging and clanging of garbage cans as their lids are being knocked askew by marauding raccoons. If the raccoon finds a certain garbage can to be a ready source of food, it will return to it night after night.

Many people enjoy these nocturnal visits and deliberately leave food out for the animals. In fact, the raccoon is probably the easiest

Curiosity and a raccoon-proofed turtle

Diamondback terrapin returning to water after laying her eggs

Yellow-spotted pond turtles are often eaten by raccoons

to attract with food offerings. My neighbors nearby, Geri and Mike Mordkin, have been feeding raccoons for several years. They began one night when a raccoon raided their garbage pail. Geri promptly put food scraps on the porch. First she left the porch light on; finally she left the door open. With more time and food, the raccoon finally got to the point where it would come into the house and pick up the food, although it preferred to eat its meal outdoors. Many people saw this happen, and the raccoon even got used to the popping of flash-bulbs, as everyone wanted photographic proof of the raccoon's visit.

The second year, the raccoon came back and surprised everyone by bringing her family with her. The three babies never became as bold as the mother, but they all crowded around the open door while the mother went into the living room and picked up pieces of apple to take to them. If everyone in the room remained still, the raccoon apparently did not care how many people sat there watching her. One

80

night when I was there, the mother came in and fed her youngsters and then they all went out and played in the oak trees growing near the porch. Because Geri was more familiar to them, she was allowed to make noise and to move about more than the others.

At the Scout camp where I live, the boys often bring from home such things as fruit, cookies, cake, and candy. These goodies are stored in their tents or in the Adirondack shelters in which the boys sleep. Almost every night the campsites are raided by both skunks and raccoons. Some of these nocturnal panhandlers travel a regular route from one tent to the next. The boys usually get a lot of enjoyment out of these visits and are more than willing to share their supplies with them. Sometimes, of course, the boys have no choice—the animals simply walk in and help themselves.

Different groups, here on week-end camping trips, have stored their bacon, butter, and meats in metal pails which they placed in a nearby brook to keep the food fresh until used. This practice had to be discontinued because of the raids by raccoons.

It is in summer when the poultry is out on range and raccoon numbers are at their peak that they cause the greatest damage. I speak from personal experience because I was raised on a farm where poultry production for both meat and eggs was our means of a living. Our farm was on the crest of a hill with woodlands surrounding the fields on three sides. We had brushy fence rows that provided protective cover for predators and made our poultry extremely vulnerable. As soon as the young chickens were large enough to survive outside, we put them out on summer pasture and housed them in range shelters.

It was at this time that our troubles would begin. In spite of hunting and trapping, and even though we kept a dog chained out in the field, our losses began. Each range shelter was made of wire covering a wooden framework; each had a solid roof. The whole structure was a foot or more off the ground. The birds were always shut up in these shelters at night and let out each morning. Still we suffered losses.

Raccoons came at night and reached through the wire to pull a bird off the perch. If the terrified bird flew out of the raccoon's grasp, it would flit to the other side of the shelter. The raccoon would then run over to the other side and catch it or another one as the chickens pressed against the wire. Sooner or later a bird would be caught, and the bandit would kill and eat it. The wire mesh was about one inch in diameter and although the chicken could not be pulled through the wire whole, pieces of it could be.

In addition to individual losses, many others died of suffocation as they piled up into a corner of the shelter in a blind panic. Some mornings there would be a bushel of dead chickens in one shelter. In an effort to prevent this, we put a light inside the shelters so that the birds could see to get back up on the perch. I am convinced that the light, instead of helping the chickens, helped the raccoons.

During the period that they tried to bankrupt us, the only good raccoon was a dead one as far as we were concerned. And this is how many poultry men feel today. Once raccoons get into the habit of feeding on poultry, they do not stop until they are killed or the chick-

"Guilty"

ens are wiped out. Unlike a fox, which will nurse its food supply along, a raccoon seems to indulge in an orgy of killing. It will return night after night until the wrath of the farmer puts an end to its depredations.

Many poultrymen bring the trouble on themselves by their method of disposing of dead chickens. Sick or diseased birds, when dead, should be burned or buried. All too often they are merely gathered up and thrown onto the fields with the manure. Some farmers have a regular dump where the chicken carcasses are discarded. It is only natural for all kinds of predatory animals to get into the habit of visiting such places. It is much easier for a wild animal to pick up a meal than it is to go out and catch one.

People are always amazed at the hole that a raccoon can squeeze through. A loose board or a tear in the wire netting is all that it needs to be able to get into a chicken coop. Many animals can pass through any hole that their heads can fit through. This is not so in the case of the raccoon, whose head is smaller than its pelvic region. Yet it is astonishing how a large furry raccoon can squeeze through a hole 3½ inches in diameter when it wants to. This also explains why many of its den trees are overlooked. Hunters expect the hole to be 10 to 12 inches wide before the raccoon can use it.

One of the best ways to determine whether or not a raccoon is using a tree or a burrow is to check for hair that has dropped out or been caught on the bark at the entrance hole. Some of the rough-barked trees I have examined have had large amounts of telltale hair on them.

Raccoons shed their coats only once a year, although some hair may be lost or pulled out at any time. The winter coat begins to loosen in March, and by the middle of April the hair has started to slough off. The hair loosens in a pattern, starting at the head and working back to the tail. Large patches may come out at one time, leaving the raccoon with a very ragged, unkempt appearance and with its tail

83

looking "ratty." Since the hairs around the head are short, the onset of shedding is hard to detect. The tail is an entirely different matter; it looks so moth-eaten and shabby that frequently the black rings cannot be seen.

Another way to discover a raccoon den tree is to take note of the scats that are so much in evidence around spots frequented by these animals. The den itself is usually kept clean, but the base of the tree and the large limbs are always covered with their dried feces. Raccoons kept in pens usually have a couple of favored voiding spots.

Raccoons also leave scats in places where they function as "calling cards." Any tree or limb lying across a stream that is regularly used by a raccoon will be covered with its scat. These advertise to one and all the recent passage of said raccoon. This habit is, of course, common to most animals, but the raccoon is the only one that I know that places these signs so close to its dwelling place.

While the young are in the den itself, there are very few creatures that would molest them and risk facing the wrath of a fighting mother 'coon. It is after the young ones first start to climb out of the den on their own that they are most subject to predation. At night the great horned owl is probably their deadliest enemy. It can swoop down and pluck a baby raccoon from a limb with no trouble at all and make off with its prey before the mother has realized that her family was under attack. The fisher, the bobcat, the mountain lion, and the wolf are predators of raccoons, but many of them have been exterminated from the raccoons' range.

The bobcat is an exception. In some areas of the United States they are still quite common, and their larger size and superior armament make them more than a match for a raccoon. I doubt that a bobcat would willingly attack a full-grown raccoon; however, they do prey upon young raccoons. A fox might also take a baby raccoon now and then, but in order to capture it, it would have to surprise the baby away from a tree. Stray dogs are also a menace, but they, too, would

Winter coat "rubbed"

have to find the youngsters out in the open.

In addition to the larger, easily visible enemies, the raccoon is also visited by many small ones. External parasites—lice and fleas of several kinds—find warmth in the furry coat of a raccoon and feed upon its blood. They are most frequently found around the animal's eyes or nose. When a raccoon is killed, these pests can often be seen leaving the cooling body. Wood ticks fasten themselves to raccoons and gorge upon their blood. A favored spot is in the crevices of the ear itself. Internal parasites range from the large roundworms, tapeworms, and lung worms to microorganisms such as the viruses. Raccoons suffer

Great horned owls prey upon young raccoons

The bobcat can kill even full-grown raccoons

The wolf is reduced today so that it is no longer a serious predator of the raccoon

The raccoon is the loser in an encounter with a skunk

from canine distemper, meningitis, septicemia, taxoplasmosis, pneumonia, and tetanus.

Periodic outbreaks of rabies may occur among raccoons, although it may not start with them. Cats, dogs, foxes, skunks, and opossums are all carriers of rabies, and any one of them can start an outbreak of the disease, which can then spread easily from species to species. The outbreak of any disease counts upon overpopulation of one kind of animal in order to get started. A number of years ago New York State had an outbreak of rabies, primarily among foxes. In order to protect both its citizens and its wildlife, New Jersey concentrated all of its professional trappers along the New York–New Jersey border, where they tried to create a buffer strip by eliminating all carnivores in the area. The plan was successful in removing the rabies threat to New Jersey, and the disease was soon controlled in New York.

Many times a raccoon accused of having rabies is actually suffer-

ing from encephalitis which is rather common. This disease also periodically incapacitates gray foxes but is less common among red foxes.

Raccoons with encephalitis may be found wandering or staggering
about at any hour of the day or night. They appear dazed and pay little
attention to anything. The disease causes an inflammation of the brain,
which then produces a paralysis of the hind quarters; hence the staggering gait. As the disease advances, the animal suffers muscular
spasms and convulsions, and finally collapses into a coma. Death follows soon afterward.

Encephalitis is transmitted by direct contact and perhaps by such
insect carriers as flies and mosquitoes. I know of a number of dogs that
contracted encephalitis from smelling and nosing around the carcass
of a raccoon that had died of the disease. So far as I know, people are
not susceptible, although I always caution anyone handling a sick
raccoon. The animal should be killed and incinerated or buried
deeply. Anyone who has touched a diseased animal should make sure
that he washes and disinfects his hands thoroughly.

It is amazing how many people will take home sick animals that
they find wandering around in the woods. The fact that they can even
approach a wild animal in its native habitat should warn them that
something may be wrong with it.

AUTUMN

THE GLORIOUSLY LIMPID DAYS of Indian summer slowly give way to the brilliance of autumn. The days become light, bright, and invigorating—the nights hold more than just a promise of winter. Trees, warned of the coming cold by the shortening of the daylight hours, evacuate the moisture from their upper extremities and put it into storage in their root systems, safe beneath the frost line. Chemical changes in the leaves set the woodlands ablaze with bright colors. The vivid crimson of the swamp maples, the shining yellow and red of the sugar maples, the muted gold of the birches, the rusty tonings of the oaks, and the somber brown of the elms create a breath-taking riot of color for all to see.

In hollows and swales, frost-rimmed grasses give shimmering testimony to the fact that laggard breezes have failed to keep the cold from settling. The warming rays of the morning sun will soon destroy the evidence. The autumn breezes set the cornfields a-rattling, the dry, unyielding leaves and stalks importuning man to hurry and partake of their golden bounty.

Raccoons, squirrels, deer, grouse, pheasants, and quail are feverishly converting the starch of grains to animal fats. Nuts cascade down, forming a mosaic on the forest floor. Each vagrant breeze tumbles

Corn is a staple of the raccoon's diet

down another red or golden apple in the orchards. There they lie, fermenting, delaying yellow jackets on the return trips to their nests. Bumblebees flit from goldenrod to goldenrod, stuffing their pollen baskets with the golden grains. Milkweed pods split asunder and expose their silken-strand seeds to the vagaries of the capricious breezes, which bear them aloft.

These are the fabulous days of autumn when a man wants to fall to his knees to offer up a prayer of thanks to God that he is alive to witness His splendid offerings.

The raccoons, too, seem to express their thanks by partaking of as much of this bounty as possible. They embark on an orgy of eating that seems to know no limits. Field corn in the milk, and even dried and dented, is the mainstay of their diet. Their foraging expeditions in some areas all but ensure crop failures. Here again it is not only what is eaten but what is wasted that takes the toll. The raccoons cause the bulk of their damage around the edges of the fields where the trees afford them the opportunity to escape if the need should arise.

Mother raccoons are still followed by their young, which have by now become small carbon copies of their parents. The young ones weigh about 10 to 12 pounds each, while the older ones average about

90

15 to 20 pounds—with more weight to be gained before the winter's rest period. A few babies born in late summer are smaller. Some females, yearlings perhaps, that missed conceiving during the regular season in February and March, have bred in the latter part of May or June. This is not a common occurrence, but it does happen often enough to convince some people that some raccoons have two litters a year. If this be true, I can find no record of it.

The late-born youngsters will weigh only 3 or 4 pounds by the time winter comes; thus, their chance of survival is almost nil. Lactating females have been found as late as November. The drain on the mothers at this late date is a handicap because it prevents them from achieving their proper body weight before the onset of winter.

Raccoons are very fond of acorns. In good years the abundance of acorns is fantastic. The fall of 1962 was just such a year. In the mountains behind my home, it was impossible to put your foot down on the ground without stepping on acorns. They were in such profusion that one actually walked on them. Reports from various sections of the country confirmed that this was not just a local bonanza but a universally good acorn year. The wild animals glutted themselves that year.

Raccoons, when they have a choice, show a decided preference for acorns from the white oaks. These have the least amounts of tannin and are less bitter than any of the other acorns.

The loss of the American chestnut from the blight dealt our wildlife a severe blow. At one time chestnuts comprised some 68 per cent of all the forest growth on lands east of the Mississippi River. These forest monarchs were, in many places, an unbroken sea of greenery, capped each spring with their multitudes of snow-white blossoms. In the autumn they covered the forest floor with their large, tasty, meaty brown nuts. Old-timers claim that today's raccoons are not as large as they used to be because of the scarcity of chestnuts. I disagree. Raccoons today have access to as much bulk food of different types as they

91

Apples too are eagerly eaten

Raccoons love to eat grapes

Grasshoppers are eaten in large numbers by raccoons

Feeling for crayfish

can possibly eat. The lack of chestnuts may be one reason why the raccoons eat more corn than they once did.

In addition to acorns, raccoons eat pecans, hickory nuts, beechnuts, and hazelnuts. Black walnuts have too thick a shell to be of interest to them—these are left for the squirrels. The opossums have to compete for their share of persimmons, because the raccoons love this sour orange fruit, too. They also eat wild grapes with gusto. If wild grapes are not available, cultivated ones are just as readily consumed.

Raccoons are the reason I have no grape juice in my freezer this winter. Down at the old farm, below my home, an untended grape vine has grown up close by a cedar. I usually wait until the grapes are a deep purple and plump enough to burst their skins. I then pick them, boil them, and freeze the juice. This year I waited a little too long, and raccoons, who must have been observing their development too, got there first.

Through September and October, insects form a large part of the raccoon's diet. At this time, grasshoppers and crickets are abundant in every pasture, hayfield, and meadow. Both skunks and raccoons consume quantities of insects without ever seeming to make a dent in

93

the total population. Both animals dig up the nests of yellow jackets and bumblebees and eat the larvae. A climber, the raccoon also preys upon the combs of the wild honey bees that frequently make their homes in a hollow or split tree or under the loose bark. The thick fur of the raccoon protects it from bee stings. It usually eats as many bees as it can during the raid and feeds on the larvae and the honey as well. It often tears rotted logs apart to secure the white insect grubs that can be found there.

In the fall, crayfish form only a small part of a raccoon's diet. A few years ago I cleaned out the reservoir that supplies our camp with its drinking water. To do this I removed the flash boards that were wedged permanently into place. After the water had rushed out, I began to fork the leaf mold and debris out of the bottom. The reservoir bottom was crawling with aquatic life all seeking cover after the withdrawal of the water. Crayfish abounded, waving their armored claws in the air as they attempted to scoot backward. Caddis fly cases and hellgrammites were also in evidence. Some of the crayfish measured well over 3 inches in length.

As I had worked in just one area, I left a large part of the pool's bottom untouched. When I returned to work the following morning, I was amazed at the raccoon tracks that literally covered every inch of the area. Pieces of crayfish lay all over. From the difference in the size of the tracks, I surmised that a female raccoon and her family had enjoyed a delightful repast the night before. Was a visit to this pool part of their nightly routine? I am sorry now that I did not count the number of crayfish remains that I saw. Lloyd Trevis on the Carmel River in California once found an area where twenty-two crayfish had been eaten in one 50-foot stretch in one night. I am sure that there were many more than that eaten in the reservoir.

The automobile often helps the raccoon to obtain its supper. Tremendous numbers of game birds and animals are killed every twenty-four hours on the nation's highways. Rabbits are the most

Raccoon scavenging along the highway

Canada goose

Mallard ducks

frequent victims, perhaps because the grass along the roadsides becomes green sooner and frequent cuttings make it more tender.

There was a period in my life when I drove a truck around the countryside picking up cans of milk at various farms and hauling them to the creamery. I kept a daily count of all wildlife that I saw which had been killed on the roads. I drove about 60 miles each day, and I sometimes saw as many as five dead rabbits in that distance. Many birds and other animals get into the habit of patrolling the highways searching for such carcasses. I have often seen raccoons at night feeding upon them. As my car approached, the raccoon invariably picked up the carcass and dragged it off into the bushes rather than take a chance of leaving it there and perhaps losing it. Raccoons themselves are often killed by cars at night as they try to cross a road.

The small game and duck-hunting seasons are another boon to the raccoon, providing it with easily obtained food. Quite frequently a hunter kills a rabbit, pheasant, or duck that runs or flies a short distance before dropping. Even though the hunter may search carefully for his quarry, he may fail to find it. The raccoon usually does better. All too frequently, hunters may shoot at too great a range or not be good enough marksmen and so only cripple their game. Under ordinary conditions it would be almost impossible for a raccoon to catch an adult rabbit, pheasant, or duck, yet it easily catches the cripples. Since many of these cripples would eventually succumb at a later date,

Meadow mouse, or vole

the raccoon actually saves them from further suffering and misery and is well fed in the process.

Around some of the lakes in California, which have tremendous flocks of ducks and geese, it was found that birds that had been crippled by hunters made up 90 per cent of the raccoon's diet during the hunting season. In connection with this, it was noted that raccoons had a penchant for chewing on the feet of the ducks and the geese even though such parts are considered inedible. Even though the birds had been dead for some time and the feet had become hard and dried, they still appealed to raccoons.

Nothing edible is overlooked by a raccoon. Meadow mice are caught in the meadows and sloughs, which the raccoon frequents. Even though the adults may escape, the raccoon locates the nest and feeds upon the young mice.

The old Dutch copper mines, famous in New Jersey, are located about 800 feet from my home. The longest horizontal shaft penetrates a hillside for about 275 feet. There is considerable moisture in the mines caused both by natural seepage and from condensation. Because of this, raccoons do not attempt to live in the mines, but they visit them frequently while hunting for food. Many insects such as daddy longlegs or "harvestmen" and some crickets can be found there. Raccoons feed upon them as well as on an occasional bat that makes the mistake of hanging too low. Although their tracks are almost always in evidence, I have never observed a raccoon in the mines.

I think that bats are eaten by raccoons in much larger numbers than we suspect. Raccoons regularly den in mines, caves, and splits in limestone outcroppings and bluffs. Many of these spots are also the ideal habitat for bats in the summer. These places also serve as hibernation spots for bats in winter.

The only food that I can recall seeing my captive raccoons refuse to eat was tomatoes. Most other animals will not touch tomatoes either, perhaps because of their acid content.

97

Entrance to the old Dutch copper mine in Warren County,
New Jersey

Little brown bat hibernating in the mines

Autumn

Under ordinary conditions, raccoons start to move about as soon as it is dark. Young raccoons are the most active and usually come out first. The mothers follow soon afterward, while old solitary males may not emerge for a couple more hours. The peak feeding period is from about eight to nine o'clock, tapering off at midnight with another flurry of activity just before dawn. As the weather becomes colder, feeding activity is increased, for raccoons make every effort to store as much fat on and in their bodies as possible.

Frequently, when food is concentrated in one area, raccoons have a tendency to congregate there. Then a sort of "pecking order" evolves. The biggest, strongest female and her young have first choice at the food. The smaller mothers give way. Single raccoons are at a disadvantage because they must face the united front of an entire family. A young raccoon, except when it is with its family group, may be set upon and driven away from food by other raccoons if it becomes separated from its family. As rival family groups approach each other, there is a general growling, flattening of the ears, and other defiant gestures. Usually the bluff works, and both groups tolerate the other's presence. Raccoons are characteristically more interested in eating than in fighting.

Raccoons I have had in captivity change from docile creatures to frenzied gluttons each fall. Their appetites apparently cannot be satisfied. Before I can ladle the food into their pans, they try to climb into the feeding pail in their efforts to get at the food. They snarl and growl if they suspect that I am going to take any food away from them. On several occasions I have weighed their food before feeding them and found that they consume three to four pounds in one night. These weights are based on regular dog meals that have been mixed with water. Perhaps they could not eat as much meat as they do meal because it would take meat longer to be digested and expelled.

The result of this ravenous appetite is a steadily growing layer of fat that forms all around the raccoon's body beneath the skin and in

99

the abdominal cavity. I have often seen this fat layer measure an inch in depth on the raccoon's back. Even the tail bone is thoroughly padded with accumulated fat.

On one occasion I killed a 21¼ pound wild raccoon and later skinned, dissected, and fleshed off every piece of fat that I could remove. I removed almost 9 pounds of pure fat from this animal. It would be safe to conclude that in the late fall fat makes up almost 50 per cent of the animal's total weight.

Removing the fat from the pelt is one of the onerous parts of hunting or trapping raccoons for their fur. All the body fat must be removed from the pelt or it will turn rancid and cause the hide to be "burned," as they say in the fur trade, and cause the hairs to slip. The fat does not stay firm when handled but has a tendency to quickly revert to a more liquid state. This fat used to be valued as a softener for leather and was also once used as a lubricant for machinery.

Despite the labor involved in removing the pelt from the raccoon, and in removing the fat from the pelt, there are hundreds of thousands of hunters across the nation who live for the time each year when they can go 'coon hunting. These hunters are from all walks of life, although by far the greatest number of them live in rural areas. Because the chances of success are so much greater, 99 per cent of them use dogs. The other 1 per cent go to haunts frequented by raccoons and attempt to find them by chance, or try to call them in by using a predator call. The predator call sounds like a rabbit that has been mortally stricken and, if used correctly, is quite efficient. Another successful call, particularly for the raccoon, sounds like the cry of a wounded sea gull and is used along the coastal areas and beaches. The response of the raccoon to these calls points up the fact that it never overlooks a chance to feed on a crippled bird or animal.

To a real dyed-in-the-wool 'coon hunter, there is no substitute for hunting with dogs, mainly hounds. There is something about the frosty nights, the dark hollows, and the musical notes of baying hounds that stir the hearts and minds of such men. I honestly believe that to such hunters the hounds are the most important part of the entire proceeding and that the raccoon is secondary. During the 1920's, when their pelts brought the phenomenal price of $18.00, raccoons were hunted almost to extinction. This was the era of the rah-rah boys with their hip flasks and their raccoon-skin coats. Everybody who was anybody bundled into one of these great coats before ambling down to the stadium to shout himself hoarse for the football team that was out there fighting for the honor of their dear old "Alma Mater."

The choice of raccoon for these coats was a good one because the fur is dense, warm, and very durable. Most of the coats were made from the skins of southern raccoons because the fur is not quite as long or as heavy as are those of the northern pelts, which were used for luxuriant collars on coats and for muffs. Today the mores of fashion have decreed against the use of the long-haired furs. It is true that the long-haired coats made one look well rounded and dumpy. The current trend is to short-haired furs, which give a much trimmer, slimmer look. Because of this, the demand for raccoon pelts has dropped to a point where the big, heavy adult pelts bring about $2.00 each. It has been found that the heavy pelts can be clipped so that most of the hair is cut off, leaving a dense, uniformly short undercoat, which is very soft and attractive. Sheared raccoon pelts look like plucked beaver pelts.

The coonskin cap was worn by many of our early settlers, although skunk and fox were also used. Daniel Boone is usually portrayed wearing a coonskin cap, yet accurate research proves that he seldom wore one. He much preferred to wear the three-cornered hat that was popular in his day. The Indians wore the various animal pelts for headgear before the coming of the white man, and this part of their apparel was adopted by the whites along with their buckskin shirts, leggings and moccasins. For use in the woods, the coonskin cap was a more fitting headpiece than the three-cornered hat because it was more durable, warmer, made no noise when it scraped against branches, and was less apt to be knocked off while its owner was running through heavy brush. And with the tail hanging down the back, it was also decorative. Both Indians and white settlers often tanned the hide so that the face of the raccoon would be on the front of the hat.

I wore a coonskin cap for many years, but only in subzero weather. The hat was so warm that it was uncomfortable in all save the coldest weather. The hat was waterproof and never got soaked through, despite the fact that it was used in heavy winter downpours.

Today's hunters hunt raccoon more for the sport than they do for the hopes of any monetary returns. Some hunters do not even shoot or take the raccoon after it is treed, although most still do.

Warm, moist nights in late fall are the very best for raccoon hunting. For one thing, the animals are active for a much longer period than they would be on colder nights, and scenting conditions are ideal. Many people believe that raccoons den up on cold nights. Until freezing weather is constant, the raccoons are active so that most nights in autumn you can find them out foraging for food.

There are probably as many types of coonhounds and dogs as there are raccoons. Dogs of almost every breed have been used, and sometimes a nondescript cur type may prove to be a very good hunter. The breeds recognized by the United Kennel Club are the Redbones, Blueticks, Black and Tans and Treeing Walkers, although, as I pointed out, almost any type of dog may do. Farm collies often make very good hunting dogs although they do not bay while tracking. This trait is very important to a 'coon hunter. Some hunters prefer a silent trailer, but the majority favor the open trailer. The silent trail hound is more deadly to the raccoon because it makes no noise while tracking down its prey. Quite frequently the silent hound will actually catch up and attack the raccoon before the raccoon even knows the dog is near or before the raccoon can escape up a nearby tree.

The open trailer, on the other hand, bays every few steps. The fresher the trail, the more excited the dog becomes and the more noise he makes. As the hound's sonorous baying reverberates throughout the darkened woodlands and bounces back off the distant hills, the hairs on the back of the hunter's neck tingle with anticipation. This sound is what he thrills to. This is the excitement of the chase. A hunter soon learns to tell his own individual hound even though it is running in a pack. The hunter can usually tell just what the dog is doing by the particular bark, bellow, bay, or yelp that the dog is giving tongue to.

There are a number of different methods employed in the hunting of the raccoon. All depend upon the hunter's knowledge of raccoons, their habits, haunts, and food supply.

Some hunters prefer to cruise a back road with the dog running on ahead. The dog checks the ditches, drain tiles, fence rows, and so forth as he trots ahead of the car. If a track is struck, the dog swings into action and so do the hunters.

It is very important that a dog be a straight 'cooner and not chase any other animal. Dogs that chase deer, fox, or rabbits when they should be hunting raccoons are only wasting the hunter's time. Following the fleeter fox or deer, the dog often runs for miles and may get lost.

After the dog strikes a raccoon's trail, some hunters stay in one spot and just listen to the dog run its quarry. Sometimes these hunters drive up and down the back roads in their cars, trying to keep their hound within hearing distance. Following a dog on foot constantly is much harder to do, and the hunter has to be in good physical condition. Yet it does offer the greatest amount of sport.

Whatever the method, the important thing is to be able to hear the dog when it has forced its quarry to take refuge and barks, "Treed." Good coonhounds stay at the tree until the hunter reaches it. Poor dogs leave the tree, and the entire hunt is spoiled. In order to encourage the dog to stay at the tree, most hunters make every effort to reach their dog soon after the raccoon is treed.

The World of the Raccoon

Meanwhile, what is happening to the raccoon while all this is taking place? The raccoon is an intelligent animal, and if the mother was hunted before and was able to escape, she can teach her youngsters many tricks. The raccoon is at a particular disadvantage. Its large, bare, plantigrade foot touches much more ground area than most animals and leaves a heavy body odor that is comparatively easy for the dogs to follow.

Young raccoons, having no previous experience, are taken in large numbers, although many hunters take only the adults. This is largely because the adult's pelt has a greater value, and because it gives the young raccoons a chance to grow up and provide a good chase for the dogs later on.

If the mother raccoon is near a den tree when she hears the baying hounds approaching through the woods, she will probably take her family and hide there. If the tree is large enough, the raccoons are safe. When the price of raccoon pelts was high, many hunters would cut down the den trees to get the raccoons. Since good den trees are used by successive generations of raccoons, this was very detrimental to the species. As a boy I saw several huge chestnut den trees that had been cut open by hunters to get at the raccoon. The trees were so large that it would have taken hours to fell them. Instead, the hunters climbed up to the hole and probed the depth of the den with a stick. Then by using an ax, a hole was cut through to the den. Today, if the raccoons den up, they are usually left there.

If an escape to a den tree or an evasive route has proven successful on one occasion, the raccoon invariably resorts to it again. The animal learns to use many tricks. It often runs along the tops of fence rows or rail fences; it climbs a tree, crawls out on a branch, and leaps off to the ground; it leaves a maze of tracks and employs many more ruses. Some raccoons just can't be taken. Raccoons that have lost a front foot in a trap are among the most difficult to hunt. Being hampered by the loss of the foot, the raccoon does not climb a tree, but

Bluetick coonhound baying "treed"

Raccoon hunter and his dogs

Large den tree destroyed by hunters who cut open the den

Treed raccoon

Raccoon swimming

seeks refuge in a ground den. This is by far the safest course for any raccoon.

When treed by the hounds, a raccoon may react in several ways. If it is a novice, it may sit up in the tree and nonchalantly watch all the commotion going on down below. Raccoons are not afraid of a bright light and sit and stare right into it. Their own eyes "shine" so that the hunter can quickly locate and shoot them. Raccoons that have been hunted before avoid looking at the light. They stretch themselves out horizontally on the limb and may be invisible from the ground. Many times they just cannot be seen.

A raccoon often tries to escape from dogs by taking to water. This is a deadly gambit because here the raccoon has the upper hand. If he can find a floating log or branch, the raccoon climbs up on it and then, reaching out, holds the pursuing dog's head underwater. If a dog catches up to a swimming raccoon in open water, the raccoon climbs right up on the dog's head and submerges it. Many dogs are drowned every year by raccoons.

Often, when pursued, a mother raccoon chases her family up a big tree, where she hopes they will stay hidden, while she attempts to divert the dogs.

Treeing a raccoon does not mean that it stays treed. Raccoons often jump out of a tree when they are not satisfied with the safety it affords them. One afternoon in September, Bud Disbrow and I were putting up signs for the Coventry Hunting Club. When I had finished, I walked back to the car but Bud hadn't returned yet. I drove down the road and found him sitting under an oak tree that was perhaps 50 feet high. When I got out of the car, Bud pointed up the tree and as my eye followed his finger, I saw a mother raccoon and her two young ones in the treetop. Bud said that he had been working farther down the fence row when the raccoons came running down the hill and up the tree. Leaving Bud sitting under the tree to keep the raccoons up there, I drove home to get my camera and electronic flash unit. This

The World of the Raccoon

I felt was a golden opportunity for photographs.

When I got back to the tree, all of the raccoons were still up there, although they were getting restless and were clambering from branch to branch. I had just started up the tree with my equipment when the female raccoon barreled out into space, hit the ground with a thud, and scampered off. Oh well, I still had two raccoons to work on. As I neared the top of the tree, one of the youngsters figured that it had had enough and departed via the aerial route, too, so now there was one. As I tried to climb over within camera range, the remaining raccoon jumped to a small sapling growing nearby and now there were none.

I climbed down out of the tree, and Bud and I pushed the sapling top over against the big tree and made all kinds of racket. Finally we forced the young raccoon to climb back into the big tree. Then while Bud held the sapling away from the big tree I climbed back up the oak. This time I was successful, and I was able to secure a number of photographs. Finally this raccoon, too, abandoned me by jumping out of the tree, and the session was over.

If a hunting dog trees a raccoon and the hunter takes a long time getting to the tree, the raccoon often jumps out and the chase goes on and on. When a raccoon is treed, he is generally shot and falls from the tree. Occasionally some hunters will climb the tree, if possible, and poke or push the raccoon from its perch with a stick. Then the dogs try to kill the raccoon on the ground. These fights are always stacked heavily in favor of the dogs because the average hound outweighs the average raccoon by about three to one. When the dogs are in a pack, the odds against the raccoon are prohibitive. The dogs do not get off unscathed however. By the time the raccoon has been killed, they know they have been in a fight.

The raccoon is strong and will fight viciously. Pound for pound, an adult raccoon can beat almost any dog going. Most coonhounds have shredded ears, and their faces are a mass of scars, proving that at one time or another they got too close to the fighting end of an angry

raccoon. The dogs try to work in pairs so that one can grab the raccoon from the rear and throw it off balance while the other dog grabs the raccoon's throat or chest for a killing bite. To circumvent an attack like this, a raccoon usually backs up against a rock or tree so that all the dogs have to come in from the front. Caught away from protection, the raccoon gets on its back so that it can fight with all of its sharp claws as well as its teeth, in the same fashion as bobcats fight.

Raccoons are also taken by trapping and as they are comparatively easy to trap, large numbers of them are taken in this manner. The trappers take advantage of two weak points in the raccoon's nature. The trappers use food baits that take advantage of the raccoon's voracious appetite in the late fall, using fish, corn, and meats. Another Achilles' heel is the raccoon's insatiable curiosity. Everything that a raccoon locates must be tasted, smelled, played with, and pawed over. If the object is shiny, a raccoon cannot resist it. Many trappers fasten a piece of a mirror or aluminum foil on the pan of a trap and place it in the shallow water at a stream's edge and cover the trap, leaving just the shiny pan exposed. Or they hang the mirror or foil from a string about 18 inches over the top of the trap and allow it to sway in the breeze. The first raccoon that comes by is almost sure to be caught.

Raccoons, because of their strength, are hard to hold in a muskrat trap. Larger traps must be used. The raccoon's forefoot is tapered and that, too, helps him to pull out. Many times after the raccoon has been trapped and its foot becomes numb, it chews its foot off and effects its escape. A raccoon that has experienced such a fate becomes trap-wise.

Their curiosity often prompts raccoons to carry off objects that they have no use for. One time I was cutting up meat for one of my pet raccoons with a sheath knife that I always wear. Sometime later I noticed that my knife was missing. I was greatly disturbed by the loss because the knife was a custom-made Randall that had been given to me by my parents. I searched and re-searched every place that I had been all that day, to no avail. I ransacked my mind trying to recall what I could have done with it. The next day I looked all over again, and at last I had to abandon my search. About a month later I happened to be cleaning out the nest box of my raccoon and putting fresh bedding in it when, lo and behold, there was my knife. The raccoon evidently had been fascinated by the shining blade and had taken the knife to its nest box. It is a wonder that the raccoon did not cut itself because I usually keep the knife razor-sharp.

Many raccoon families split up in the late fall just before winter sets in. The hunting season influences this. Many families are broken up when members are killed by hunters. Other families are split when raccoons seek to escape from hunting dogs and are driven so far away that they do not regroup.

By late fall the young raccoons weigh almost 15 pounds, having acquired their winter supply of fat. Their coats of fur are prime, too, since all of the pigment has moved up the hair stalk. Adult raccoons are usually prime by the first of November, but it generally takes the

Raccoon holding two dogs at bay.

Raccoon fighting on its back

young another month. The young ones have had their permanent teeth since October, and at this time no wear can be detected. Slight wear on the tips of the canine teeth is usually a good indication of a two-year-old raccoon, while considerable wear suggests that the raccoon is three years old or older.

It is imperative at this time that the young raccoons that are going to winter by themselves seek out an appropriate den. Natural dens such as hollow trees, stumps, logs, caves, and ledges are used. Man-made structures, such as mines, deserted homes, garages, and barns, are often utilized. Home on the farm, we once had a raccoon that wintered under the floor beneath the hay mow. This is a common occurrence, borne out by the records of many observers.

Some of the dens that are chosen leave a lot to be desired. I know of several that are in hollow trees that have no top so that all of the rain and snows pour in on top of the sleeping animal. Raccoons have also been known to climb up into a hollow limb, where they have to maintain a hold to keep themselves from falling out.

Although they prefer to nest in trees, many raccoons winter in woodchuck burrows. By now, most of the woodchucks have retired to a side room of their dens, which they then seal off to prevent intrusion from any outsiders. There, safe and snug, the woodchuck has curled up into a ball and has dropped into the torpid state of hibernation. It little knows nor cares that a young raccoon may be utilizing the rest of the burrow as its winter home.

A young raccoon trying a den for size

WINTER

THE SOLSTICE HAS PASSED and the daylight hours grow longer, yet temperatures continue to plummet downward and winter continues to tighten its icy grip over most of our country. Wind-whipped snows sculpture cornices along the roadsides, piling up the depths with loads picked up from exposed hilltops. These snows play important but varying roles in the lives of wild animals.

To the meadow vole, snow is a boon. Safe beneath the fluffy blanket of white, this little rodent is busily laying out an intricate network of passageways. Now, protected from the prying eyes of the predators, such as the owl, the hawk, the fox and the cat, the meadow vole can enjoy this respite and concentrate on food. Its passages lead to the various edible grasses, to areas where seeds may be gleaned, and to its warm, fluffy nest. The winds and the cold are also locked out by a white barrier. This is truly the meadow vole's time of ease.

To the deer, shivering in the draws and valleys, the deep snows are often a death sentence. As the cold increases, deer forsake their regular haunts and seek out the hollows to escape the biting winds. As the snow feathers down and increases in depth, the movements of the deer are hampered. The available food is soon eaten, and a network of paths has to be trampled out in the attempt to find more. This need for

114

Winter quarters

In cold weather raccoons are lethargic

115

Raccoons are reluctant to walk in deep snow

Raccoons in the southern states remain active all winter

increased effort on the part of the rapidly weakening deer forces many to lie down and accept whatever fate has in store for them. Thus the soft, fluffy blanket becomes as effective a jail as any of steel or concrete. In the spring the bleached bones show where the deer tried and failed.

To the average raccoon, snug in his hollow den tree, the snow is immaterial. The raccoon couldn't care less, nor does it have to. A provident Nature has allowed the raccoon to acquire its store of body fat to be consumed when just such conditions prevail. The raccoon is not a hibernator, although it will den up and remain inactive for several weeks on end. Its body metabolism does not decrease as in the case of the true hibernating animal such as the woodchuck; nor does its body temperature drop. The raccoon becomes lethargic, but is easily roused if something disturbs its slumbers.

The temperature, more than anything else, is the controlling factor in a raccoon's denning up. I have found the dividing line between the raccoon's remaining active and its denning up to be 26 to 28 degrees Fahrenheit. As long as the bulk of the weather remains above this point, the raccoon will range about all winter. When the temperature drops below this point, the raccoon retires until the weather moderates. A sudden break in below-26-degree weather, which sends the temperature creeping upward, will also activate the raccoon. If there is deep snow on the ground, the raccoon stays in its den even though the temperature rises above freezing. Being comparatively short-legged, the raccoon realizes that it would soon bog down and be at a disadvantage if it attempted to negotiate the soft, deep snow. Florida raccoons have longer legs in proportion to their body size than do the northern raccoons. This is not for snow travel but is governed by the basic mathematical law that makes northern mammals bulkier in size so that they can conserve body heat. As soon as the snow thaws slightly, then freezes with a crust, the raccoon can again become mobile.

Wind is another factor that limits the raccoon's activities. When the wind rises up to 8 to 10 miles per hour, the raccoon curtails its feeding; and as the velocity increases, it stops feeding entirely. The fact that in cold weather the wind makes the cold more penetrating is important, yet most mammals become increasingly nervous and change their habits as the wind increases in force. Animals that depend upon scent or sound for protection from danger are seriously handicapped by the variable gusty winds that send trees crashing to the ground and pound thousands of branches together so that all signs of stalking predators are effectively drowned out.

Wildlife can easily predict an approaching storm by the change in the barometric pressure, sometimes even before our scientific instruments record the change. At such times they feed much earlier and more constantly and retire back to shelter as soon as possible.

As the winter wears on, the raccoon accepts lower temperatures and moves about as its body becomes acclimated to the cold. By the time breeding season comes, in January or February, the male moves in almost zero weather.

Not all raccoons den up in the wintertime. Those inhabiting our southern states remain active all winter and are constantly hunting for food in the swamps and mangrove thickets. The southern raccoons do not lay on as much of a store of body fat either for the simple reason that they do not need it.

Some of the northern raccoons are not able to den up for the bulk of the winter either. Late-born youngsters that come into the winter unprepared, as far as body size and fuel reserves go, are forced to leave their dens almost constantly to search for food. Enforced denning because of deep snow reduces their body weight alarmingly, and the majority of them succumb before springtime.

While many raccoon families split up in the fall, many others do not. Now there is a distinct advantage to their having stayed together, for they can utilize each other's body heat in order to keep warm. Sometimes raccoons of different families den together, although most groupings are related. There have been records of two or more adult

Raccoon tracks in snow. Front foot on left, hind foot on the right

Raccoon tracks

A yearling male

females occupying the same den, and this must be considered a case of mutual advantage.

When the weather does moderate, the raccoons bestir themselves and seek out whatever food is available. They feed heavily upon trapped muskrats, if such activity is being carried on in their area. In the southern marshes the damage raccoons do to trapped fur bearers is considerable. The only recourse left to the trapper is to trap the raccoon, too. Winter-killed deer carcasses are a mecca for raccoons in the northern forests. Any of the carnivores are quick to take advantage of these finds, and almost all animal tracks lead directly to them.

My raccoons, kept in outdoor pens, require little or no attention for long periods in the wintertime. I usually feed all of my animals in the middle of the afternoon, when the temperature has risen as high as it is going to get, and while I have the daylight to see what I am doing. My pet skunk will come out to feed every day, no matter how cold it is outside, but the raccoons refuse to budge. If I open their pens and put some food in their pans to tempt them into activity, my efforts are usually met with a few sleepy yawns—nothing more. They respond to the slightest sound and will wake up and watch me, but they make no effort to come out. If I place a piece of meat in the den with them, they sometimes eat it, yet if I place the meat six inches from the den, they just ignore it and let it freeze.

The response to noise has also been noted in wild raccoons. I have often pounded on a hollow tree in the wintertime to see if any raccoons occupy it. Quite frequently the raccoon peers out to see who is making all that racket. I have five different den trees right now that I check regularly to see how the raccoons in each den are doing.

Many of my friends have had raccoons come in and raid their bird feeders. Suet, which is usually fastened to a tree trunk for the woodpeckers, appeals to raccoons. Once a raccoon has found a source of suet, there is hardly ever any left for the birds. I solved this problem by suspending my suet from a string so that only the birds could reach it.

Raccoons will also feed on the grain and seed put out for birds, and they particularly relish peanuts and cracked corn. Remedial action has to be taken if raccoons start to visit your feeding stations, because they clean them out overnight, trying to satisfy the demands made by their tremendous appetites. Perhaps the best and easiest way to discourage their forays is to place a feeder on a metal pipe with a large circular metal guard beneath it.

As the winter wears on, the coat of the raccoon becomes "rubbed." The animal breaks off or wears down some of the individual hairs by such normal activities as climbing, passing through small holes, or scratching itself. Even the fur of an animal that is curled up and sleeping may wear off where it touches against the rough inside of the den tree. Just the constant regular rising and falling of the raccoon's breathing will rub the hair against the wood and cause it to break.

121

The World of the Raccoon

And so the winter passes on without too much effort on behalf of the raccoon until the breeding season begins. In Louisiana and some of the other southern states breeding activity may take place as early as late December or early January. Over most of the raccoon's range, however, the breeding urge is started in late January and February. The males are affected first, and driven on by the hormonal changes in their bodies, they set out to seek the females.

The average range of a raccoon may be only a square mile, yet during the breeding season the male may travel much greater distances, holing up at daybreak wherever it may happen to be. He searches out every hollow tree in his area, and his tracks lead to all of the big basswoods, beeches, maples, oaks, and sycamores because these are all ideal den trees. Tracks in the snow have been followed which showed that one male covered eight miles in one night of searching for a mate.

Male raccoons are polygamous; the females are not. Although the female may be visited by different males, she accepts the one male that she considers her mate and drives off the unwanted males. Captive females that have been separated from their mates almost always refuse to mate with a newly introduced male. If her mate is taken from her, a captive female may call and cry almost constantly and pace her cage looking for a way to escape so that she can join the male. If her mate is placed in an adjoining pen, she takes great comfort in being able to reach through and touch him. Rival males often fight over a female, but being the victor does not necessarily guarantee the privileges that are usually thought to be attendant upon winning. The female makes the final choice, not the male.

Yearling males are not sufficiently developed sexually to be able to breed. Breeding males are always two years old or older. However, about 40 per cent of the yearling females breed, although their first litter usually is small in number. It is easy to tell a breeding female because after the lactation period her teats are not only larger but dark in color instead of a virginal pink.

When the male locates a receptive female, he usually moves into her quarters to stay with her. It usually takes from one to two weeks before the female is ready to accept him. Breeding may take place for three or four consecutive days, after which it takes another week or two until the swelling of the female's glands subside.

Periodically there are reports by people, and some that are even carried in the newspapers, that a raccoon and a cat have mated and produced offspring. This is a biological impossibility, since these animals are too distantly related to make fertilization possible.

After having been bred, the female usually goes back into her lethargic half-sleep for the rest of the winter. The male is active for a much longer period, starting earlier and continuing later so that most of the winter is over before he settles down to await the coming of spring.

RACCOON AND MAN

THE EARLIEST AMERICANS, the Indians, thought highly of the raccoon. Their very livelihood depended upon their thorough knowledge of all of the plants and wild creatures that lived in the same area as they did. They were very keen observers, and what they saw of the raccoon, they liked very much. Many of their legends told how the raccoon outsmarted the other animals of the forests. The Sioux Indian name for the raccoon was *wica*, which means "a male of the human species" or "little man." The raccoon's hind foot looked like their own, it used its forepaws the way they did their hands, and it just seemed smart enough to be a little man.

Captain John Smith writing in 1617 declared, "The chief beasts of Virginia are Beares, lesse than those in other places, deere like ours, aroughcun much like a badger, but living on trees like a squirrell." His observations and simile were good because the raccoon does look like a long-legged, long-tailed badger.

Captain Smith goes on to report that Chief Wahunsonacock, often called Powhatan, after the Indian federation he headed, had a great robe made of raccoon skins. This robe was square and all of the tails were left on the individual pelts. This robe covered an elevated platform upon which the chief sat before the ceremonial fire

124

when he was holding court among his people. The raccoon skin robe was considered to be a symbol of his high station in life.

The early settlers found many uses for the raccoon. The skins were made into robes, hats, or other garments and were used in bartering in lieu of money. In 1788 the settlers of the mountainous section of eastern Tennessee split from the parent state and set up one of their own which they called the "State of Franklin." Since they had no money in the treasury and taxes were paid in barter goods, the newly formed state had no paper currency. To pay its governing officers, the legislature decreed that these gentlemen be paid in skins of a value relative to the job held and the office filled. The governor received the highest salary at the rate of 1000 deer skins annually. The secretary to the governor was to be paid 500 raccoon skins, while the clerk of the House of Commons was to receive 200 raccoon skins annually.

The raccoon always has been, and is today, an important food item. The method of cooking depends upon the age of the animals. They are broiled, boiled, fried, stewed, and roasted. Roasted raccoon is probably the most popular method of preparation. One precaution must be taken in preparing the meat for use: every bit of available fat must be peeled off the carcass. The raccoon is such a fat animal that this involves a lot of work, but it must be done if the true flavor of the meat is to be appreciated. Ordinarily, a fur buyer today prefers to buy the pelts already skinned, fleshed, and dried. Yet some of them now offer to pay 50 cents apiece more if the raccoon is brought into them whole and as soon after being killed as possible. The carcasses are then taken to city areas that have a large Negro population, and here they are sold. Raccoon thus provides these people with a very good source of inexpensive meat.

People are always interested in the numbers of the various animals in what is now the United States before the coming of the white man. These figures are always very hard to arrive at and almost impossible to prove. Ernest Thompson Seton sets the figure for the number of raccoons at about 5 million. He arrived at that number by taking the results of Poland's Fur Trade Reports for the London fur sales. These reports show that from 1850 to 1890 there were about 500,000 raccoon skins sold annually from North America. From other sales records and reports he figured that perhaps only 50 per cent of the yearly raccoon fur harvest ever reached the London fur sales. This would have made the total yearly kill about 1 million raccoons. Seton further figured that the raccoon could only stand a yearly reduction in numbers of about 20 per cent in order to hold its population at the numbers present in his time, and they were holding their own. Thus, he concluded, the raccoon population at that time must have been about 5 million.

These figures are most interesting and so is Seton's method of arriving at them. Experts today figure that the raccoon is as abundant now as it has ever been, and their figure is also set at 5 million. Actual reports show that about 1 million raccoons are killed by hunters and trappers each year in the United States today, so that the raccoon seems to be maintaining the *status quo.*

The raccoon's greatest asset is its adaptability. It is really an omnivorous creature, eating whatever is available, as I have tried to point out. Many more intelligent animals have had to give way before the onslaught of civilization because they could not adapt to the new situations that were created.

As the forests were cut down, the raccoon changed its way of life. When the chestnuts died off, it changed its diet, and when the hunting pressure slackened, it was quick to take advantage of it.

That raccoons have been successful can be easily seen from the fact that their numbers have been increasing. The late 1920's and the 1930's saw the low point in their numbers. Since around 1940, their rise has been meteoric.

In Maine, in 1935, the Game Department, in an effort to combat the loss of raccoons, stocked the offshore island of North Haven with five pairs of these animals. This island, 6 miles long and about 4 miles wide and 14 miles from the coastal town of Rockland, made a very good experimental site because most factors could be kept constant and no predators existed there. In a ten-year period the raccoons had multiplied to the point where, in spite of regular hunting seasons, their numbers could not be controlled. It was estimated that the raccoon population had grown to more than 400, and the inhabitants of the island pleaded with the state to change the law so that raccoons could be brought under control.

Long Island, near Kodiak Island in Alaska, has also been stocked with raccoons. Although these animals have never normally ranged that far north, they are, at last reports, thriving.

Yaeger and Rennels did an extensive study on the raccoons along the lush river bottoms in the Pere Marquette Wildlife Experimental Area in Illinois. They found this to be ideal habitat and calculated that the raccoons had responded to these conditions to the extent that there were about 53 raccoons to the square mile. This area has rich soil, swamps, potholes, heavy copses of thickets, and an abundance of den trees. Little disturbance by man and a plentiful supply of food have made this sort of a raccoon heaven.

F. W. Stuewer studying raccoons in Michigan found that there was one raccoon to each 16.2 acres on a total study area of 1235 acres. While not as plentiful as were the raccoons on the Marquette tract, they averaged out to be about 40 to the square mile.

As amazing as these figures are, however, they do not even compare favorably with the number of raccoons at the Swan Lake National Wildlife Refuge in Mississippi. Here an intensive live-trapping and hunting program was conducted for 4½ days in January of 1948. In addition to the Game Commission's own men, local men were allowed to bring in their dogs and participate. The raccoons were caught in live traps or were treed by dogs and then captured alive. This concentrated effort produced 100 raccoons from 102 acres, and it was

estimated that this was only 60 per cent of the population that was present at that time. Many of the raccoons had sought shelter in den trees and burrows and could not be taken. This is the largest concentration of raccoons that I have been able to find on record.

During flood times along the Mississippi flowage, it is comparatively easy to catch a hundred raccoons in one night on the levees or from the trees and shrubs. It must be remembered, though, that this is an unusual condition and one that forces a concentration of all the wildlife of the area on to higher ground.

Synthetic fibers and the skins of short-furred animals that are used by clothing manufacturers today have given the raccoon more protection than the game laws by reducing the demand for its fur, with the resulting drop in the price paid for it.

Indiana, Missouri, and Michigan are the top three raccoon-producing states today with Indiana leading the way with 170,000 pelts

128

sold each year. In the 1957–58 winter, 112,284 raccoons were taken in Missouri. Although the price went as high as $2.00 for adults, the pelts averaged out to 85 cents apiece for a total value of $95,441.00. The 1961 figure for New Hampshire was 1,370 raccoons for an average of $1.62, while in the same year 6,325 raccoons were taken in North Dakota for an average price of $2.09. The variations in price depends upon the market, the location of the state where the pelts were taken, the size of the individual animal, as well as the care given to the pelts by the hunters and trappers. Raccoon pelts have been sold under such fur-trade names as Alaska Sable or Alaska Bear.

The low price of the fur will allow bigger raccoons to be taken, for fewer hunters mean that more of the animals will live longer and have a greater chance of reaching full size. Although both Maine and Minnesota are famous for the large size of their raccoons, Texas also has some very large ones. The local area around Orono, Maine, has for years produced uniformly larger raccoons than almost any other locality, yet the hunting pressure is probably greater there because of this fact.

In an effort to gain greater knowledge of the raccoon for better management, many of our states have carried on extensive studies of the raccoon in an attempt to develop reliable methods of judging this animal's age. The wear evidenced on the canine teeth has not been too satisfactory. The latest development has been the use of X-ray equipment to photograph the epiphyses, or cartilaginous joints, of the wrist of the raccoon's forefoot. Many parts of the human body fuse together with advancing age, and this is also true of raccoons. At ten months of age there is a very broad joint mark that tends to close and disappear by the time that the raccoon is two years old. More accurate techniques for calculating the animal's age have still to be developed.

Raccoon farming has been tried many times, particularly during the late 1920's, when the price of the pelts was at an all-time high,

129

Leonard Lee Rue III bottle feeding

Leonard Lee Rue IV and friend

but most of these ventures were doomed to failure. It cost so much to feed the raccoons and took so long for the animals to reach full size that more money—not to say effort—was expended than could be realized by the sale of the fur. Raccoons are still raised on a few farms, but now such farming is done to supply the market with animals to be used as pets.

Raccoons while young make fascinating pets, but they should not be kept beyond two years of age, especially if they are to be handled. Beyond that age they become sullen and temperamental, and I bear the scars to prove it.

There was one particular male raccoon that I raised from infancy. It had been given to me by a neighbor. I fed it first with an eye-dropper, then advanced it to a bottle, and gradually got it to drink from a saucer. I used to handle the little fellow constantly and carry it about in my pocket. When it got bigger, some of the boys used to carry it about sitting on the top of their heads as a real live Davey Crockett hat.

I often took the raccoon swimming with me. Although he could swim well, he was always reluctant to do so if he could avoid it. When I waded out into deep water, he would run along the shore, back and forth, back and forth, crying piteously at the thought of being left behind. Finally he would plunge in and swim out to me. This was not the most pleasant experience because he would climb up my bare arms or chest by sinking his claws into the flesh. These were just superficial scratches, however.

It is impossible to let young raccoons have the freedom of a house because nothing is sacred to them. They think draperies and curtains are put there to test their climbing ability. Their dashes up the drapes either put long pulls and tears in the material or end with a sudden crash as entire fixtures are pulled loose from the window casing.

My wife is particular, and the very thought of having a raccoon walk across the kitchen table is enough to get both the raccoon and me thrown out of the house. And of course where did my raccoon like to go? Up on the kitchen table, the counters, and the sink. Raccoons like sinks, bathtubs, and toilet bowls because of their penchant for playing in the water.

My office desk, which is always far from being neat, is inevitably a shambles by the time a raccoon has spent two minutes investigating everything on it. Thank God the top of the ink bottle was tight! All in all, it is not a good idea to bring raccoons into the house. They can usually tear more apart in ten minutes than anyone can straighten up in an hour.

My pet raccoons have always gotten along well with my dogs. If anything, the raccoons would take advantage of them even to the extent of eating the dogs' food. They, in turn, perhaps, would have liked to give the raccoons a good drubbing but realized that I would probably punish them. Raccoons are more alert than dogs, but this is probably because the raccoons are from wild stock while the dogs have been domesticated for eons. On several occasions I have stood on the second-story porch of our home and called to the animals below. The raccoons always looked up and noticed me long before the dogs did. The dogs were as quick to hear me but while they would look around, the raccoons would look up. Objects above the ground level do not interest dogs very much because they cannot climb.

At different times when my sons were small, they would be playing in their wading pool when the raccoons would move in and join them. On the whole, the raccoons have been treated like members of the family. The first sign of belligerence generally showed up if you crossed them or denied them something they wanted. Just like children.

I have never believed in letting a young raccoon or dog bite me in play. This habit is too hard to break later when the animal is

James Keith Rue sharing his tub

larger and capable of doing harm. A raccoon's canine teeth come to a perfect point and are needle-sharp, and it does not take much pressure to break a human's skin. I also clip the toenails on the raccoon for the same reason. Trouble really starts after a raccoon reaches the age of two, because it is then mature and becomes particularly aggressive in the breeding season.

The male raccoon I spoke of earlier was a little over two years old and weighed 21 pounds when he scarred me. It was a warm day in the fall and my shirt sleeves were rolled up. Some friends dropped in, and of course they wanted to see my animals. I took the raccoon out of his pen and showed him to everyone, then let him climb up to his accustomed place on my shoulder. When we were ready to go back into the house, I reached up to get the raccoon, but he was not ready to come down. In a fit of anger he bit through my ear, his canines passing each other, and as I removed him, he slashed at my wrists. All of a sudden he realized that he had been naughty and

133

remorsefully covered his face with his paws.

When he escaped about a month later, I felt that it was all for the best. Although this happened several years ago, I still have his marks upon me.

This past summer my nephew, Robert Rowe, raised a pair of raccoons that had been given to his father after the mother raccoon had been killed by a farm collie. Bobby spent all of his time with his pets, and those little fellows became the tamest raccoons that I have ever seen. They even became mascots for the local football team, although they were terrified by the noise made by the marching band. With the coming of cold weather the raccoons started to break out of their pen even though it was much warmer than any den tree could ever be. Although they got out at night, they were usually back by morning. All raccoons will den up, if at all possible, before dawn washes clear the morning sky.

One morning, one of the raccoons did not come home, and Bobby thought that it probably had fallen into the river and, not being able to clamber back up on the ice, had drowned. The remaining raccoon seemed quite wet too. The next day this raccoon died, and when I examined it, I found that it had a number of perforations in its stomach and other internal injuries. The animal had probably been bitten by dogs, and the wet appearance of the fur was probably caused by the dogs' saliva. A neighbor had a large number of dogs in a pen, and I imagine the raccoons made the mistake of climbing over into the pen.

Sterling North in his wonderfully warmhearted book *Rascal* tells of his delightfully nostaglic reminiscences of his pet raccoon. His experiences were similar to those of anyone who raises these interesting creatures. In the end Mr. North had to release his pet, and so does almost everyone else.

Many people think it is cruel to set an animal free after it has been raised in captivity. With many animals, perhaps this would be true, especially if the animal was released in the middle of winter. Of all the animals that can make the transition, the raccoon can most easily do so.

Mammalogists recognize nineteen different subspecies of the raccoons that live in various parts of the United States. These are geographic varieties, which may be different in color or size owing to the influences of different climate or to isolation. The classification of the North American raccoon follows that of Gerrett S. Miller and Remington Kellogg in *List of North American Recent Mammals*.

1. *Procyon lotor lotor* lives from Nova Scotia south through the New England states to North Carolina and west to Lake Michigan, Indiana, Illinois, western Kentucky, and eastern Tennessee.

2. *Procyon lotor maritimus* is limited to the marsh areas of the Delmarva Peninsula of Virginia, Delaware, and Maryland.

3. *Procyon lotor solutus* frequents the islands and coastal region of South Carolina.

4. *Procyon lotor litoreus* frequents the islands and the coastal strip of Georgia.

5. *Procyon lotor elucus* ranges from southern Georgia to Florida, except for the southwestern part of that state.

6. *Procyon lotor marinus* inhabits the southwestern part of Florida and the Keys of the Ten Thousand Islands.

7. *Procyon lotor inesperatus*, in the southeastern Florida Coast keys, ranges from Virginia Key south to Lower Matecumbe Key, including Key Largo.

8. *Procyon lotor auspicatus* is the raccoon of the southern Florida coast keys, particularly the Key Vaca groups.

9. *Procyon lotor incautus* inhabits the Big Pine Key Group near the southwestern end of the Florida Keys.

10. *Procyon lotor varius* lives in southwestern Kentucky, Tennessee, Mississippi, northern Louisiana, Alabama, northwestern Florida, and western Georgia.

11. *Procyon lotor hirtus* lives over a tremendous range, from the eastern slopes of the Rocky Mountains to Lake Michigan and from southern Manitoba, Ontario, Alberta, and Saskatchewan, all the way south to southern Oklahoma and Arkansas.

12. *Procyon lotor megalodus* frequents the coastal region of southern Louisiana.

13. *Procyon lotor fuscipes* ranges over most of Texas, southern Arkansas and Louisiana, except the Mississippi delta region, and south into northern Mexico.

14. *Procyon lotor mexicanus* is primarily a Mexican raccoon, which enters the United States in the southern portions of Arizona, New Mexico, and west Texas.

15. *Procyon lotor pallidus* lives in the Colorado and Gita river valleys from the delta north to southeastern Nevada, parts of Utah, Colorado, and New Mexico.

16. *Procyon lotor psora* lives in most of California and eastward to the eastern slope of the Sierra Nevadas in Nevada.

17. *Procyon lotor pacificus* lives within northern California, western Oregon, and Washington, and southwestern British Columbia.

18. *Procyon lotor excelsus* ranges from the Snake River drainage in southeastern Washington, to eastern Oregon, southern Idaho, northern Nevada, and the river valleys of northeastern California.

19. *Procyon lotor vancouverensis* has a range limited to Vancouver Island, British Columbia.

It is claimed that man is the most adaptable creature on earth. This may be true, yet more and more men are becoming specialists, with a greater concentration of effort and knowledge in ever more isolated areas. The raccoon has proved that to survive, one must be adaptable; one must be able to cope with whatever situations are presented. Our own ultimate survival may rest on our remembering that this is as true for man as for the raccoon.

BIBLIOGRAPHY

Arthur, Stanley C. *The Fur Animals of Louisiana*. New Orleans, La.: Louisiana Department of Conservation, 1931.

Baker, Rollin H.; Newman, Coleman C.; and Wilke, Ford. "Food Habits of the Raccoon in Eastern Texas," *Journal of Wildlife Management* (Vol. 9, 1945).

Bourliere, Francois. *Mammals of the World*. New York: Alfred A. Knopf, 1955.

Brooks, David M. *Fur Animals of Indiana* (Bulletin No. 4). Indianapolis, Indiana: Indiana Department of Conservation, 1959.

Burns, Eugene. *The Sex Life of Wild Animals*. New York: Rhinehart & Co., Inc., 1953.

Butterfield, Robert T. "Some Raccoon and Groundhog Relationships," *Journal of Wildlife Management* (Vol. 18, 1954).

Cahalane, Victor H. *Mammals of North America*. New York: The Macmillan Co., 1947.

Camp, Raymond R. *The Hunter's Encyclopedia*. Harrisburg, Pa.: Stackpole & Heck, Inc., 1948.

Bibliography

Cory, Charles B. *The Mammals of Illinois and Wisconsin.* (Publication 153). Chicago: Field Museum of Natural History, 1912.

Dorney, Robert S. "Ecology of Marsh Raccoons," *Journal of Wildlife Management* (Vol. 18, 1954).

Giles, Leroy W. "Food Habits of the Raccoon in Eastern Iowa," *Journal of Wildlife Management* (Vol. 4, 1940).

Gunderson, Harvey L., and Beer, James R. *The Mammals of Minnesota.* Minneapolis, Minn.: University of Minnesota Press, 1953.

Hamilton, William J., Jr. *American Mammals.* New York: McGraw-Hill Book Co., Inc., 1939.

———. "The Summer Food of Minks and Raccoons on the Montezuma Marsh," New York, *Journal of Wildlife Management* (Vol. 4, 1940).

———. *The Mammals of Eastern United States.* Ithaca, N. Y.: Comstock Publishing Co., Inc., 1943.

Jackson, Hartley H. T. *Mammals of Wisconsin.* Madison, Wisc.: University of Wisconsin Press, 1961.

McSpadden, J. Walker. *Animals of the World.* Garden City, N. Y.: Garden City Publishing Co., Inc., 1942.

Miller, Gerrit S., and Kellogg, Remington. *List of North American Recent Mammals* (United States National Museum Bulletin No. 205) Smithsonian Institution, Washington, D.C., 1955.

Morgan, Ann H. *Field Book of Animals in Winter.* New York: G. P. Putnam's Sons, 1939.

Nelson, E. W. *Wild Animals of North America.* Washington, D.C.: National Geographic Society, 1930.

Palmer, Dr. E. Lawrence. *Fieldbook of Mammals.* New York: E. P. Dutton & Co., Inc., 1957.

Sanderson, Glen C., "Methods of Measuring Productivity in Raccoons," *Journal of Wildlife Management* (Vol. 14, 1950).

———. *Techniques for Determining Age of Raccoons.* (Biological Notes No. 45) Urbana, Illinois: Illinois Natural History Survey, 1961.

Sanderson, Glen C., and Thomas, Richard M., "Incidence of Lead in Lives of Illinois Raccoons," *Journal of Wildlife Management* (Vol. 25, 1961).

Sanderson, Ivan T., *Living Mammals of the World.* Garden City, N. Y.: Hanover House, 1956.

Schwartz, Charles W., and Schwartz, Elizabeth R. *The Wild Mammals of Missouri.* Kansas City, Mo.: University of Missouri Press, 1959.

Seton, Ernest Thompson. *Lives of Game Animals.* Boston: Charles T. Branford Co., 1953.

Sharp, Ward M., and Sharp, Louise H., "Nocturnal Movements and Behavior of Wild Raccoons at a Winter Feeding Station," *Journal of Mammalogy* (Vol. 27, 1956).

Silver, Helenette. *A History of New Hampshire Game and Furbearers.* Concord, N. H.: New Hampshire Fish and Game Department, 1957.

Stone, Witmer, and Cram, William Everett. *American Animals.* New York: Doubleday, Page and Co., 1902.

Stuewer, Frederick W. "Reproduction of Raccoons in Michigan," *Journal of Wildlife Management* (Vol. 7, 1943).

Thomas, Earl M. *Wyoming Fur-Bearers.* (Bulletin No. 4) Cheyenne, Wyo.: Wyoming Game and Fish Department, 1954.

Trippensee, Ruben Edwin. *Wildlife Management.* New York: McGraw-Hill Book Co., Inc., 1953.

Bibliography

Whitney, Leon F. "The Raccoon—Some Mental Attributes," *Journal of Mammalogy* (Vol. 14, 1933).

Whitney, Leon F., and Underwood, Acil B. *The Raccoon.* Orange, Conn.: Practical Science Publishing Co., 1952.

Wilson, Kenneth A. "Raccoon Predation on Muskrats Near Currituck, North Carolina," *Journal of Wildlife Management* (Vol. 17, 1953).

Yeager, Lee E., and Rennels, R. G. "Fur Yield and Autumn Foods of the Raccoons in Illinois River Bottom Lands," *Journal of Wildlife Management* (Vol. 7, 1943).

INDEX

Index

Index